Don't Forget to Fly

AUTHORS

Elaine Mei Aoki
Virginia A. Arnold
James Flood
James V. Hoffman
Diane Lapp
Miriam Martinez

Annemarie Sullivan
 Palincsar
Michael Priestley
Nancy Roser
Carl B. Smith

William H. Teale
Josefina Villamil
 Tinajero
Arnold W. Webb
Peggy E. Williams
Karen D. Wood

MACMILLAN/McGRAW-HILL SCHOOL PUBLISHING COMPANY

NEW YORK   CHICAGO   COLUMBUS

AUTHORS, CONSULTANTS, AND REVIEWERS

WRITE IDEA! Authors

Elaine Mei Aoki, James Flood, James V. Hoffman, Diane Lapp, Ana Huerta Macias, Miriam Martinez, Ann McCallum, Michael Priestley, Nancy Roser, Carl B. Smith, William Strong, William H. Teale, Charles Temple, Josefina Villamil Tinajero, Arnold W. Webb, Peggy E. Williams

The approach to writing in Macmillan/McGraw-Hill Reading/Language Arts is based on the strategies and approaches to composition and conventions of language in Macmillan/McGraw-Hill's writing-centered language arts program, WRITE IDEA!

Multicultural and Educational Consultants

Alma Flor Ada, Yvonne Beamer, Joyce Buckner, Helen Gillotte, Cheryl Hudson, Narcita Medina, Lorraine Monroe, James R. Murphy, Sylvia Peña, Joseph B. Rubin, Ramon Santiago, Cliff Trafzer, Hai Tran, Esther Lee Yao

Literature Consultants

Ashley Bryan, Joan I. Glazer, Paul Janeczko, Margaret H. Lippert

International Consultants

Edward B. Adams, Barbara Johnson, Raymond L. Marshall

Music and Audio Consultants

John Farrell, Marilyn C. Davidson, Vincent Lawrence, Sarah Pirtle, Susan R. Snyder, Rick and Deborah Witkowski

Teacher Reviewers

Terry Baker, Jane Bauer, James Bedi, Nora Bickel, Vernell Bowen, Donald Cason, Jean Chaney, Carolyn Clark, Alan Cox, Kathryn DesCarpentrie, Carol L. Ellis, Roberta Gale, Brenda Huffman, Erma Inscore, Sharon Kidwell, Elizabeth Love, Isabel Marcus, Elaine McCraney, Michelle Moraros, Earlene Parr, Dr. Richard Potts, Jeanette Pulliam, Michael Rubin, Henrietta Sakamaki, Kathleen Cultron Sanders, Belinda Snow, Dr. Jayne Steubing, Margaret Mary Sulentic, Barbara Tate, Seretta Vincent, Willard Waite, Barbara Wilson, Veronica York

ACKNOWLEDGMENTS

The publisher gratefully acknowledges permission to reprint the following copyrighted material:

"Be an Inventor," "Behind the Scenes," "Something to Keep the Ears Warm," "Hero of the Safety Hood," "Fabulous Frisbee," and "Introducing Weekly Reader's Young Inventors" from BE AN INVENTOR by Barbara Taylor, illustrated by David Wenzel. Copyright © 1987 by Field Publications. Reproduced by permission of Harcourt Brace Jovanovich, Inc.

"Ben and Me" from BEN AND ME by Robert Lawson. Copyright © 1939 by Robert Lawson. Copyright © renewed by John W. Boyd. By permission of Little, Brown and Company.

"The Best Bad Thing" from THE BEST BAD THING by Yoshiko Uchida. Copyright © 1983 by Yoshiko Uchida. Reprinted with permission of Margaret K. McElderry Books, an imprint of Macmillan Publishing Company.

Cover use of THE BEST BAD THING, THE HAPPIEST ENDING, and A JAR OF DREAMS all by Yoshiko Uchida. Covers by Kinuko Craft and used with permission of the artist.

"Breaker's Bridge" from THE RAINBOW PEOPLE by Laurence Yep. Text copyright © 1989 by Laurence Yep. Reprinted by permission of Harper-Collins Publisher.

"Change" from RIVER WINDING by Charlotte Zolotow. Copyright © 1970 by Charlotte Zolotow. Reprinted by permission of HarperCollins Publishers.

Book covers for THE CHRONICLES OF NARNIA by C. S. Lewis. Reproduced with the permission of the Macmillan Publishing Company.

"City" from THE LANGSTON HUGHES READER by Langston Hughes. Copyright © 1958 by Langston Hughes. Copyright renewed 1986 by George Houston Bass. Used by permission of Harold Ober Associates Incorporated.

"Dear Mr. Henshaw" from DEAR MR. HENSHAW by Beverly Cleary. Copyright © 1983 by Beverly Cleary. Used by permission of William Morrow & Company, Inc./Publishers, New York.

"Dive to the Coral Reefs" from DIVE TO THE CORAL REEFS: A NEW ENGLAND AQUARIUM BOOK, written by Elizabeth Tayntor, Paul Erickson and Les Kaufman. Copyright © 1986 by The New England Aquarium. Reprinted by permission of Crown Publishers, Inc. Permission also from Mews Books Ltd. for New England Aquarium.

Book cover for FALCON BOW by James Houston. Reprinted with the permission of Margaret K. McElderry Books, an imprint of Macmillan Publishing Company. Copyright © 1986 by James Houston.

"For Poets" by Al Young. Copyright © 1968 by Al Young. Reprinted with permission of the author.

"Fossils" from SOMETHING NEW BEGINS by Lilian Moore. Copyright © 1982 by Lilian Moore. Reprinted by permission of Atheneum Publishers, an imprint of Macmillan Publishing Company.

Book cover for THE GARDEN OF ABDUL GASAZI by Chris Van Allsburg. Copyright © 1979 by Chris Van Allsburg. Reprinted by permission of Houghton Mifflin Co. All rights reserved.

(continued on page 607)

Macmillan/McGraw-Hill School Division
10 Union Square East
New York, New York 10003

Printed in the United States of America
ISBN 0-02-178761-1 / 5, L.11
3 4 5 6 7 8 9 RRW 99 98 97 96 95 94 93

To my nieces and nephews and to
Stuart Francis and Rachel DeMaster,
for teaching me that young people have
stories to share every bit as beautiful
as the oldest and wisest among us.

Paul Rogers

To my sister Elizabeth, who led me
towards freedom when she taught me
how to read.

Eve Spencer

UNFORGETTABLE PLACES

48
The Talking Eggs

A folk tale from the American South
retold by Robert D. San Souci, illustrated by Jerry Pinkney
Coretta Scott King Honor Book, 1990; Caldecott Honor Book, 1990

Blanche's life of hard work for her mother and her lazy sister Rose is miserable. Then one day she helps an old woman who introduces her to a world of magic and riches.

20
The Wreck of the *Zephyr*

A fantasy
written and illustrated by Chris Van Allsburg
New York Times Best Illustrated Children's Books of the Year, 1983

Caldecott Award–winning illustrator

How did the wreck of a sailboat come to lie on top of a cliff high above the sea? An old sailor tells a surprising story.

TRANSFORMATIONS

AGAINST THE ODDS

226
Breaker's Bridge

A Chinese folk tale from *The Rainbow People*
by Laurence Yep, illustrated by David Wisniewski
Boston Globe–Horn Book Honor Book for Nonfiction, 1989

Newbery Honor Award–winning author

The emperor demands that Breaker build a bridge spanning a treacherous river or lose his head. Breaker tries and tries again. But when a mysterious old man comes along, Breaker learns that things change and yet do not change.

210
The Marble Champ

A short story from the book *Baseball in April*
by Gary Soto, illustrated by Ken Spengler
ALA Best Books for Young Adults, 1990; Booklist Editors' Choice; Horn Book Fanfare Selection, 1990

Lupe dreams of the day when she'll win at some sport, any sport. When she sets her sights on a marble championship, will she roll her way to success?

Getting to know you

286
The Best Bad Thing

An excerpt from the novel
by Yoshiko Uchida, illustrated by Kinuko Y. Craft
ALA Notable Children's Book, 1983

Nothing seems worse to Rinko than spending the summer harvesting cucumbers with her mother's eccentric friend, Mrs. Hata. Nothing, that is, until tragedy strikes.

318
Dear Mr. Henshaw

An excerpt from the novel
by Beverly Cleary, illustrated by R. J. Shay
Newbery Medal, 1984

Will Leigh Botts, who wants to become an author, win lunch with a famous author? He isn't sure what his chances are, but he does know one author he'd love to meet.

Way To Go

390
The House of Dies Drear

An excerpt from the mystery
by Virginia Hamilton, illustrated by Thomas Blackshear
**Ohioana Book Award, 1969; Edgar Allan
Poe Award, 1969**

Newbery Award–winning author

Could Thomas really be imagining those eerie
sounds he hears in the tunnel beneath his
family's new home? Maybe, but the house seems
to hold strange secrets.

368
Klondike Fever

A chapter from ***GOLD! The Klondike Adventure***
a social studies book
by Delia Ray

Gold! This magic word sent thousands of fortune
seekers north to the Klondike. Not all of them
found riches, but they all did find adventure.

410
Long Claws: An Arctic Adventure

An excerpt from the book
written and illustrated by James Houston

Facing a life-or-death struggle with a
grizzly bear, two Inuit children summon up more
courage than they ever dreamed they had.

434
The Incredible Journey

An excerpt from the novel
by Sheila Burnford, illustrated by Lars Justinen
**ALA Notable Children's Book, 1961;
Lewis Carroll Shelf Award, 1971**

Separated from his companions and nearly
drowned by a powerful flood, a cat finds safety
and comfort with a welcoming family. But the
pull of his journey is still strong.

More to Explore

Books from the Classroom Library

ARE YOU SURE?

460
How to Think Like a Scientist: Answering Questions by the Scientific Method

An excerpt from the book
by Stephen P. Kramer, illustrated by Kim Behm

How do scientists figure things out? Stephen P. Kramer shares their method with you so that you, too, can think like a scientist.

480
The News About Dinosaurs

Excerpts from the science book
by Patricia Lauber
School Library Journal Best Book, 1989; Booklist Editors' Choice, 1989; Outstanding Science Trade Book for Children, 1989

What's the latest word on dinosaurs? Patricia Lauber knows. In this selection she separates fact from fiction to give you all the news about dinosaurs.

CONTENTS

FORGETTABLE PLACES :•

My memory of that place is as clear as the sunlight on the sea and as haunting as shadows in the wood—and yet I've never even been there.

ANONYMOUS

19

The Wreck of the Zephyr

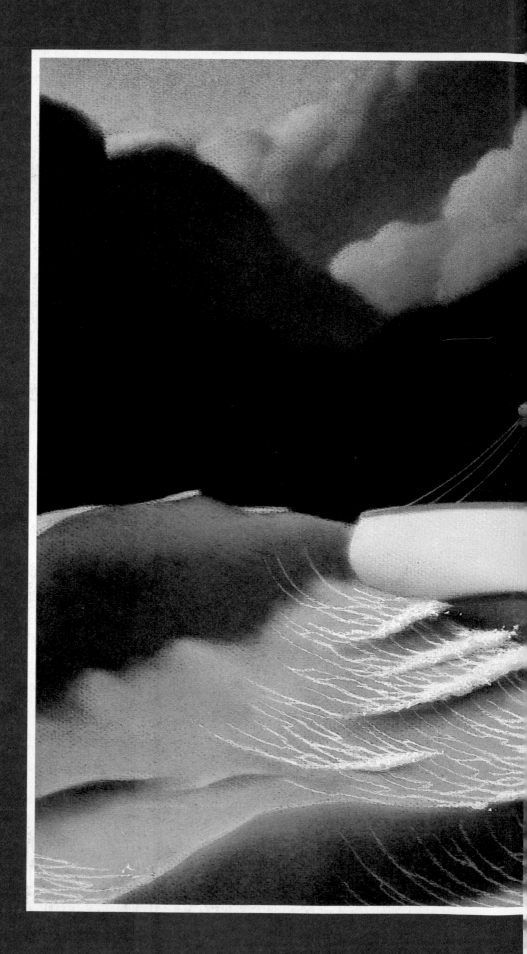

Written and illustrated by **CHRIS VAN ALLSBURG**

Once, while traveling along the seashore, I stopped at a small fishing village. After eating lunch, I decided to take a walk. I followed a path out of the village, uphill to some cliffs high above the sea. At the edge of these cliffs was a most unusual sight—the wreck of a small sailboat.

An old man was sitting among the broken timbers, smoking a pipe. He seemed to be reading my mind when he said, "Odd, isn't it?"

"Yes," I answered. "How did it get here?"

"Waves carried it up during a storm."

"Really?" I said. "It doesn't seem the waves could ever get that high."

The old man smiled. "Well, there is another story." He invited me to have a seat and listen to his strange tale.

"In our village, years ago," he said, "there was a boy who could sail a boat better than any man in the harbor. He could find a breeze over the flattest sea. When dark clouds kept other boats at anchor, the boy would sail out, ready to prove to the villagers, to the sea itself, how great a sailor he was.

"One morning, under an ominous sky, he prepared to take his boat, the *Zephyr,* out to sea. A fisherman warned the boy to stay in port. Already a strong wind was blowing. 'I'm not afraid,' the boy said, 'because I'm the greatest sailor there is.' The fisherman pointed to a sea gull gliding overhead. 'There's the only sailor who can go out on a day like this.' The boy just laughed as he hoisted his sails into a blustery wind.

"The wind whistled in the rigging as the *Zephyr* pounded her way through the water. The sky grew black and the waves rose up like mountains. The boy struggled to keep his boat from going over. Suddenly a gust of wind caught the sail. The boom swung around and hit the boy's head. He fell to the cockpit floor and did not move.

"When the boy opened his eyes, he found himself lying on a beach. The *Zephyr* rested behind him, carried there by the storm. The boat was far from the water's edge. The tide would not carry it back to sea. The boy set out to look for help.

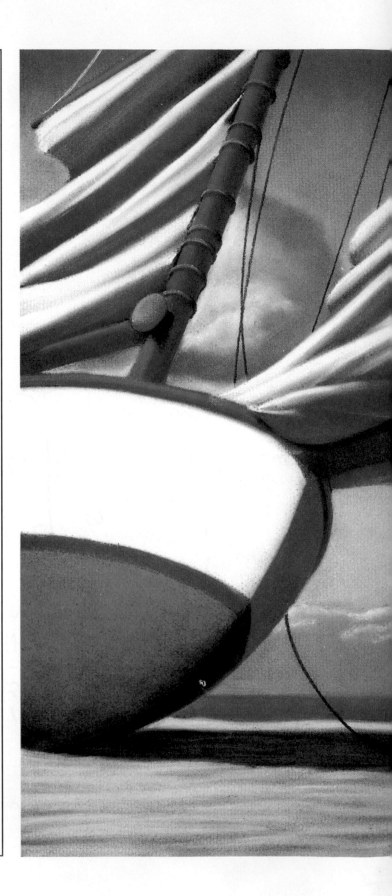

"He walked for a long time
and was surprised that he didn't
recognize the shoreline. He climbed
a hill, expecting to see something
familiar, but what he saw instead
was a strange and unbelievable
sight. Before him were two boats,
sailing high above the water.
Astonished, he watched them glide
by. Then a third sailed past, tow-
ing the *Zephyr*. The boats entered
a bay that was bordered by a large
village. There they left the *Zephyr*.

"The boy made his way down
to the harbor, to the dock where
his boat was tied. He met a sailor
who smiled when he saw the boy.
Pointing to the *Zephyr* he asked,
'Yours?' The boy nodded. The sailor
said they almost never saw
strangers on their island. It was
surrounded by a treacherous reef.
The *Zephyr* must have been carried over the reef by the storm. He
told the boy that, later, they would
take him and the *Zephyr* back over
the reef. But the boy said he would
not leave until he learned to sail
above the waves. The sailor told
him it took years to learn to sail
like that. 'Besides,' he said, 'the
Zephyr does not have the right
sails.' The boy insisted. He pleaded
with the sailor.

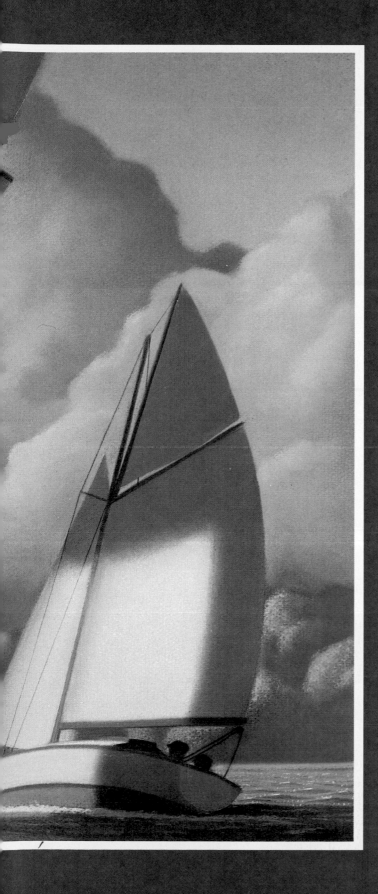

"Finally the sailor said he would try to teach him if the boy promised to leave the next morning. The boy agreed. The sailor went to a shed and got a new set of sails.

"All afternoon they sailed back and forth across the bay. Sometimes the sailor took the tiller, and the boat would magically begin to lift out of the water. But when the boy tried, he could not catch the wind that made boats fly.

"When the sun went down they went back to the harbor. They dropped anchor and a fisherman rowed them to shore. 'In the morning,' the sailor said, 'we'll put your own sails back on the *Zephyr* and send you home.' He took the boy to his house, and the sailor's wife fed them oyster stew.

"After dinner the sailor played the concertina. He sang a song about a man named Samuel Blue, who, long ago, tried to sail his boat over land and crashed:

'For the wind o'er land's ne'er steady nor true,
*   an' all men that sail there'll meet Samuel Blue.'*

"When he was done with his song, the sailor sent the boy to bed. But the boy could not sleep. He knew he could fly his boat if he had another chance. He waited until the sailor and his wife were asleep, then he quietly dressed and went to the harbor. As he rowed out to the *Zephyr,* the boy felt the light evening wind grow stronger and colder.

35

"Under a full moon, he sailed the *Zephyr* into the bay. He tried to remember everything the sailor had told him. He tried to feel the wind pulling his boat forward, lifting it up. Then, suddenly, the boy felt the *Zephyr* begin to shake. The sound of the water rushing past the hull grew louder. The air filled with spray as the boat sliced through the waves. The bow slowly began to lift. Higher and higher the *Zephyr* rose out of the water, then finally broke free. The sound of rushing water stopped. There was only the sound of wind in the sails. The *Zephyr* was flying.

"Using the stars to guide him, the boy set a course for home. The wind blew very hard, churning the sea below. But that did not matter to the *Zephyr* as she glided through the night sky. When clouds blocked the boy's view of the stars, he trimmed the sails and climbed higher. Surely the men of the island never dared fly so high. Now the boy was certain he was truly the greatest sailor of all.

"He steered well. Before the
night was over, he saw the moonlit
spire of the church at the edge of
his village. As he drew closer to
land, an idea took hold of him. He
would sail over the village and
ring the *Zephyr*'s bell. Then everyone would see him and know that
he was the greatest sailor. He flew
over the tree-topped cliffs of the
shore, but as he reached the
church the *Zephyr* began to fall.

"The wind had shifted. The boy
pulled as hard as he could on the
tiller, but it did no good. The wind
shifted again. He steered for the
open sea, but the trees at the cliff's
edge stood between him and the
water. At first there was just the
rustle of leaves brushing the hull.
Then the air was filled with the
sound of breaking branches and rip-
ping sails. The boat fell to the
ground. And here she sits today."

"A remarkable tale," I said, as the old man stopped to relight his pipe. "What happened to the boy?"

"He broke his leg that night. Of course, no one believed his story about flying boats. It was easier for them to believe that he was lost in the storm and thrown up here by the waves." The old man laughed.

"No sir, the boy never amounted to much. People thought he was crazy. He just took odd jobs around the harbor. Most of the time he was out sailing, searching for that island and a new set of sails."

A light breeze blew through the trees. The old man looked up. "Wind coming," he said. "I've got some sailing to do." He picked up a cane, and I watched as he limped slowly toward the harbor.

Meet Chris Van Allsburg

Van Allsburg holding a scene from his book
The Polar Express

Chris Van Allsburg is probably one of the most successful book illustrators in the United States—yet he almost didn't become an illustrator at all. As a child, he loved to draw and was good at it. But by the time he went to college, he wanted to be a lawyer. His talent won out. He took one drawing class "as a lark," and a year later he began serious study to become a professional artist.

His first book, *The Garden of Abdul Gasazi,* won eight book awards, and his second book, *Jumanji,* won a Caldecott Medal, the top award given for children's book illustration. A 1985 book, *The Polar Express,* won another Caldecott Medal—making Van Allsburg the first artist ever to win two.

Part of Van Allsburg's success may have to do with his idea of what an artist should be. "To me, the artist's role is as a magician who can make strange things happen," he explains. "The opportunity to create a small world between two pieces of cardboard . . . is exciting and rewarding." He has turned this fascination into books and illustrations that are both weird and wonderful. In *Jumanji,* a jungle board game comes to life—with frightening results. In the award-winning *The Wreck of the Zephyr,* you saw how Van Allsburg's "magic" turned a simple sailboat into something marvelous to behold.

TO THE

Board the S.S. Friendship, and set forth on a mission to the moon.
Countdown: **10...9...8...**
At a Challenger Learning Center, students experiment in
a realistic-looking space capsule and mission-control
room. The youngsters concentrate on simulating the
exploration of space and landing on the moon.

**Mission Control at the
Challenger Center in
Houston, Texas**

Are you calm?
Can you speak
clearly and read
carefully? On the
Communications
Team, it's your job
to send messages
between space and
Mission Control.

MOON

Are you a pathfinder?

Do you like to make decisions? The Navigation Team identifies star constellations, puts the Space Life Station into its orbit around the moon, chooses a landing site, and lands the lunar module on the moon's surface.

Do you like robots?

On the Remote Team, you operate a robot arm. The robot arm collects rock and soil samples from the moon's surface. You must classify and analyze the samples in the glovebox laboratory.

Are you good at solving problems?

On the Life Support Team, you conduct tests to check the air, water, and power systems on board. You keep the environment safe and comfortable for the crew.

Take your work stations. Complete the countdown:

...3...2...1...BLASTOFF!

A path to the moon

From my front door there's a path to the moon
that nobody seems to see
tho it's marked with stones & grass & trees
there's nobody sees it but me.

You walk straight ahead for ten trees or so
turn left at the robin's song
follow the sound of the west wind down
past where the deer drink from the pond.

You take a right turn as the river bends
then where the clouds touch the earth
close your left eye & count up to ten
while twirling for all that you're worth.

And if you keep walking right straight ahead
clambering over the clouds
saying your mother's & father's names
over & over out loud

you'll come to the place where moonlight's born
the place where the moonbeams hide
and visit all of the crater sites
on the dark moon's secret side.

From my front door there's a path to the moon
that nobody seems to see
tho it's marked with stones & grass & trees
no one sees it but you & me.

b p Nichol

THE TALKING EGGS

A Folktale from the American South

retold by *Robert D. San Souci*
pictures by *Jerry Pinkney*

Back in the old days there was a widow with two daughters named Rose and Blanche. They lived on a farm so poor, it looked like the tail end of bad luck. They raised a few chickens, some beans, and a little cotton to get by.

Rose, the older sister, was cross and mean and didn't know beans from birds' eggs. Blanche was sweet and kind and sharp as forty crickets. But their mother liked Rose the best, because they were alike as two peas in a pod—bad-tempered, sharp-tongued, and always putting on airs.

The mother made Blanche do all the work around the place. She had to iron the clothes each morning using an old iron filled with hot coals, chop cotton in the afternoon, and string the beans for supper. While she'd be doing these chores, her mama and sister would sit side by side in rocking chairs on the shady porch, fanning themselves and talking foolishness about getting rich and moving to the city, where they could go to fancy balls wearing trail-train dresses and lots of jewels.

One hot day the mother sent Blanche to the well to fetch a bucket of water. When the girl got there, she found an old woman wrapped in a raggedy black shawl, near fainting with the heat.

"Please, child, give me a sip of water," the old woman said. "I'm 'bout to die of thirst."

"Yes, aunty," said Blanche, rinsing out her bucket and dipping up some clean, cool well water. "Drink what you need."

"Thank you, child," said the old woman when she'd taken swallow after swallow of water. "You got a spirit of do-right in your soul. God is gonna bless you." Then she walked away down the path that led to the deep woods.

When Blanche got back to the cabin, her mother and sister hollered at her for taking so long.

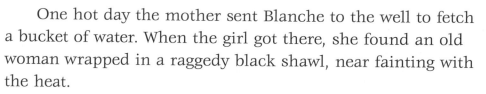

"This water's so warm, it's near boilin'," shouted Rose, and she dumped the bucket out on the porch.

"Here your poor sister's near dyin' for a drop of cool water," her mother screamed, "and you can't even bring her that little thing."

Then the two of them scolded and hit Blanche until the frightened girl ran away into the woods. She began to cry, since she didn't have anywhere to go, and she was scared to go home.

Suddenly, around a bend in the path came the old woman in the raggedy black shawl. When she saw Blanche, she asked kindly, "What's made you cry so, you poor child?"

"Mama and sister Rose lit into me for something that wasn't my fault," said Blanche, rubbing tears off her cheek. "Now I'm afraid to go home."

"Hush, child! Stop your crying. You come on home with me. I'll give you supper and a clean bed. But you got to promise you won't laugh at anything you see."

Blanche gave her word of honor that she wouldn't laugh. Then the old woman took her by the hand and led her deep into the backwoods. As they walked along the narrow path, bramble bushes and tree branches opened wide in front of them, and closed up behind them.

Soon they came to the old woman's tumble-down shack. A cow with two heads, and horns like corkscrews, peered over a fence at Blanche and brayed like a mule. She reckoned it was a pretty strange sight, but she didn't say anything, not wanting to hurt the old woman's feelings.

Next, she saw that the yard in front of the cabin was filled with chickens of every color. Some were hopping about on one leg, some running about on three or four or even more. These chickens didn't cluck, but whistled like mockingbirds. But strange as all this was, Blanche stuck by her promise not to laugh.

When they got inside the cabin, the old woman said, "Light the fire, child, and cook us some supper." So Blanche fetched kindling from the woodpile outside the back door.

The old woman sat down near the fireplace and took off her head. She set it on her knees like a pumpkin. First she combed out her gray hair, then she plaited it into two long braids. Blanche got pretty scared at this. But the woman had been nothing but kind to her, so she just went on lighting the fire.

After a bit the old woman put her head back on her shoulders and looked at herself in a sliver of mirror nailed to the cabin wall. "Um-m-m-hum!" she said, nodding. "That's better."

Then she gave Blanche an old beef bone and said, "Put this in the pot for supper."

Now Blanche was near starving, and the bone looked like a pretty sad meal for the two of them, but she did what the old woman said. "Shall I boil it for soup, aunty?" she asked.

"Look at the pot, child!" the old woman said, laughing.

The pot was filled with thick stew, bubbling away.

Next the woman gave Blanche only one grain of rice and told her to grind it in the stone mortar. Feeling mighty foolish Blanche began to pound the grain with the heavy stone pestle. In a moment the mortar was overflowing with rice.

When they had finished supper, the old woman said, "It's a fine moonshiny night, child. Come with me."

They sat themselves down on the back porch steps. After a time dozens of rabbits came out of the underbrush and formed a circle in the yard. The men rabbits all had frock-tail coats, and the lady rabbits had little trail-train dresses. They danced, standing on their hind feet, hopping about. One big rabbit played a banjo, and the old woman hummed along with it.

Blanche kept time by clapping along. The rabbits did a square dance, a Virginia reel, and even a cakewalk. The girl felt so happy, she never wanted to leave. She sat and clapped until she fell asleep, and the old woman carried her inside and put her to bed.

When Blanche got up the next morning, the old woman told her, "Go milk my cow."

The girl did what she was told and the two-headed cow with the curly horns gave her a bucket of the sweetest milk she'd ever tasted. They had it with their morning coffee.

61

"You gotta go home now, child," the old woman said to Blanche, who was washing the breakfast dishes. "But I tell you, things will be better from here on out. And since you are such a good girl, I got a present for you.

"Go out to the chicken house. Any eggs that say, 'Take me,' you go ahead and take. But if you hear any say, 'Don't take me,' you leave them be. When you get near home, throw those eggs one after another over your left shoulder so they break in the road behind you. Then you'll get a surprise."

When Blanche got to the little chicken house, she found all the nests filled with eggs. Half were gold or silver or covered with jewels; half looked no different from the eggs she got from her chickens back home.

All the plain eggs told her, "Take me." All the fancy ones cried, "Don't take me." She wished she could take just *one* gold or silver or jeweled egg, but she did what the old woman told her and only scooped up the plain ones.

She and the old woman waved good-bye to each other, then Blanche went on her way. Partway home she began to toss the eggs one at a time over her left shoulder. All sorts of wonderful things spilled out of those eggs: now diamonds and ru-bies, now gold and silver coins, now pretty silk dresses and dainty satin shoes. There was even a handsome carriage that grew in a wink from the size of a matchbox—and a fine brown-and-white pony that sprouted from the size of a cricket to draw it.

Blanche loaded all these lovely things into the carriage and rode the rest of the way home like a grand lady.

When she got back to the cabin, her mother and sister just gawked at her new finery. "Where did you get all these things?" her mother asked, making Rose help Blanche carry the treasures inside. That evening the mother cooked dinner for the first time since Blanche was old enough to hold a skillet. All the time telling Blanche what a sweet daughter she was, her mama got the girl to tell about the old woman and the cabin in the woods and the talking eggs.

When Blanche was asleep, the mother grabbed Rose and told her, "You gotta go into the woods tomorrow mornin' and find that old aunty. Then you'll get some of those talkin' eggs for yourse'f so's you can have fine dresses and jewels like your sister. When you get back, I'll chase Blanche off and keep her things myse'f. Then we'll go to the city and be fine ladies like we was meant to be."

"Can't we just run her off tonight so's I don't have to go pokin' through the woods lookin' for some crazy ol' aunty?" Rose whined.

"There's not near enough for two," her mother said, getting angry. "You do as I say and don't be so contrary."

So the next morning Rose set out drag-foot into the woods. She dawdled mostly, but soon met the old woman in her raggedy black shawl.

"My sweet little sister Blanche tol' me you got a real pretty house an' all," said Rose. "I'd 'preciate to see it."

"You can come with me if you've a mind to," said the old woman, "but you got to promise not to laugh at whatever you see."

"I swear," said Rose.

So the old woman led her through the bramble bushes and tree branches into the deep woods.

But when they got near the cabin and Rose saw the two-headed cow that brayed like a mule and the funny-looking chickens that sang like mockingbirds, she yelled, "If there ever was a sight, that's one! That's the stupidest thing in the world!" Then she laughed and laughed until she nearly fell down.

"Um-m-m-hum," said the old woman, shaking her head.

Inside, Rose complained when she was asked to start the fire, and she wound up with more smoke than flame. When the old woman gave her an old bone to put in the pot for supper, Rose said crossly, "That's gonna make a mighty poor meal." She dropped it in the pot, but the old bone remained a bone, so they only had thin soup for supper. When the old woman gave her one grain of rice to grind in the mortar, Rose said, "That sad speck won't hardly feed a fly!" She wouldn't lift the pestle, so they had no rice at all.

"Um-m-m-hum!" the old woman muttered.

Rose went to bed hungry. All night long she heard mice scratching under the floor and screech-owls clawing at the window.

In the morning the old woman told her to milk the cow. Rose did, but she made fun of the two-headed creature and all she got was a little sour milk not fit for drinking. So they had their breakfast coffee without cream.

When the old woman lifted her head off her shoulders to brush her hair, quick as a wink Rose grabbed that head and said, "I'm not gonna put you back t'gether 'til you give me presents like my sister got."

"Ah, child, you're a wicked girl," said the old woman's head, "but I got to have my body back, so I'll tell you what to do.

"Go to the chicken house and take those eggs that say, 'Take me.' But leave be the ones that cry, 'Don't take me.' Then you toss those eggs over your right shoulder when you're on your way home."

To be sure the old woman wasn't playing her a trick, Rose set the old woman's head out on the porch while her body sat groping around the cabin. Then she ran to the chicken house. Inside, all the plain eggs cried, "Take me," while all the gold and silver and jeweled ones said, "Don't take me."

"You think I'm fool enough to listen to you and pass up the prettiest ones? Not on your life!" So she grabbed all of the gold and silver and jeweled eggs that kept yelling, "Don't take me," and off she ran into the woods with them.

As soon as she was out of sight of the old woman's cabin, she tossed the eggs over her right shoulder as fast as she could. But out of the shells came clouds of whip snakes, toads, frogs, yellow jackets, and a big, old, gray wolf. These began to chase after her like pigs after a pumpkin.

Hollering bloody murder Rose ran all the way to her mother's cabin. When the woman saw the swarm of things chasing her daughter, she tried to rescue her with a broom. But the wasps and wolf and all the other creatures wouldn't be chased off, so mother and daughter high-tailed it to the woods, with all the animals following.

When they returned home, angry and sore and stung and covered with mud, they found Blanche had gone to the city to live like a grand lady—though she remained as kind and generous as always.

For the rest of their lives Rose and her mother tried to find the strange old woman's cabin and the talking eggs, but they never could find that place again.

MEET ROBERT D. SAN SOUCI

When his car broke down in Pecos, Texas, Robert D. San Souci had no idea that it would turn out to be a lucky "break." To escape from the roadside heat, San Souci went into a nearby mission. His first novel, *Emergence,* about Indians of the Southwest, grew out of what he learned there.

San Souci was fascinated by Native American legends and folklore. His first children's book, *The Legend of Scarface,* retold a Blackfoot Indian myth. The book won two awards for the story and another for its illustrator, San Souci's brother, Daniel. The two also worked together on *The Song of Sedna,* based on an Eskimo myth. The brothers have separate projects, too. Jerry Pinkney illustrated *The Talking Eggs* for Robert D. San Souci.

MEET JERRY PINKNEY

If you were to visit the home of artist Jerry Pinkney, you might witness the unusual way in which he plans his work. Before he begins to draw pictures for a book, Jerry and his family and friends put on costumes and act out the events of the book. As they do this, he takes photographs, which he refers to later when doing the actual drawings.

Pinkney is the only artist ever to have illustrated three Coretta Scott King Award-winning books. He has won other awards and prizes, including a Caldecott Honor for *The Talking Eggs.*

73

UNDER THE SUN

The Desert Is Theirs
by Byrd Baylor
illustrated by Peter Parnall
Aladdin, 1975

This is for hawks
that like only
the loneliest canyons
and lizards
that run
in the hottest sand
and
coyotes
that choose
the rockiest trails.

AND BY THE MOON

A mumble of thunder complained from far away and then the clouds parted and the moon rode free. Instantly the mist was luminous, and Egan, with a gasp, felt as if he had suddenly been tucked inside a bubble.

Kneeknock Rise
by Natalie Babbitt
Farrar, Straus & Giroux, 1970

The VOYAGE OF THE DAWN TREADER

By C.S. Lewis

Illustrated by Amy Hill

Cousin Eustace is a rather whiny and annoying boy. Unfortunately, Lucy and Edmund Pevensie must spend the entire summer at his house. They would much rather be in the enchanted land of Narnia, which they have visited twice before.

The land of Narnia is one of literature's most unforgettable places. And the means of getting there are—like Narnia itself—magical, mysterious, and entirely unexpected.

he story begins on an afternoon when Edmund and Lucy were stealing a few precious minutes alone together. And of course they were talking about Narnia, which was the name of their own private and secret country. Most of us, I suppose, have a secret country but for us it is only an imaginary country. Edmund and Lucy were luckier than other people in that respect. Their secret country was real. They had already visited it twice; not in a game or a dream, but in reality. They had got there of course by magic, which is the only way of getting to Narnia. And a promise, or very nearly a promise, had been made them in Narnia itself that they would some day get back. You may imagine that they talked about it a good deal, when they got the chance.

They were in Lucy's room, sitting on the edge of her bed and looking at a picture on the opposite wall. It was the only picture in the house that they liked. Aunt Alberta didn't like it at all (that was why it was put away in a little back room upstairs), but she couldn't get rid of it because it had been a wedding present from someone she did not want to offend.

It was a picture of a ship—a ship sailing nearly straight towards you. Her prow was gilded and shaped like the head of a dragon with wide open mouth. She had only one mast and one large, square sail which was a rich purple. The sides of the ship—what you could see of them where the gilded wings of the dragon ended—were green. She had just run up to the top of one glorious blue wave, and the nearer slope of that wave came down towards you, with streaks and bubbles on it. She was obviously running fast before a gay wind, listing over a little on her port side. (By the way, if you are going to read this story at all, and if you don't know already, you had better get it into your head that the left of a ship when you are looking ahead, is *port,* and the right is *starboard.*) All the sunlight fell on her from that side, and the water on that side was full of greens and purples. On the other, it was darker blue from the shadow of the ship.

"The question is," said Edmund, "whether it doesn't make things worse, *looking* at a Narnian ship when you can't get there."

"Even looking is better than nothing," said Lucy. "And she is such a very Narnian ship."

"Still playing your old game?" said Eustace Clarence, who had been listening outside the door and now came grinning into the room. Last year, when he had been staying with the Pevensies, he had managed to hear them all talking of Narnia and he loved teasing them about it. He thought of course that they were making it all up; and as he was quite incapable of making anything up himself, he did not approve of that.

"You're not wanted here," said Edmund curtly.

"I'm trying to think of a limerick," said Eustace. "Something like this:

> "Some kids who played games about Narnia
> Got gradually balmier and balmier—"

"Well, *Narnia* and *balmier* don't rhyme, to begin with," said Lucy.

"It's an assonance," said Eustace.

"Don't ask him what an assy-thingummy is," said Edmund. "He's only longing to be asked. Say nothing and perhaps he'll go away."

Most boys, on meeting a reception like this, would either have cleared out or flared up. Eustace did neither. He just hung about grinning, and presently began talking again.

"Do you like that picture?" he asked.

"For Heaven's sake don't let him get started about Art and all that," said Edmund hurriedly, but Lucy, who was very truthful, had already said, "Yes, I do. I like it very much."

"It's a rotten picture," said Eustace.

"You won't see it if you step outside," said Edmund.

"Why do you like it?" said Eustace to Lucy.

"Well, for one thing," said Lucy, "I like it because the ship looks as if it was really moving. And the water looks as if it was really wet. And the waves look as if they were really going up and down."

Of course Eustace knew lots of answers to this, but he didn't say anything. The reason was that at that very moment he looked at the waves and saw that they did look very much indeed as if they were going up and down. He had only once been in a ship (and then only as far as the Isle of Wight) and had been horribly seasick. The look of the waves in the picture made him feel sick again. He turned rather green and tried another look. And then all three children were staring with open mouths.

What they were seeing may be hard to believe when you read it in print, but it was almost as hard to believe when you saw it happening. The things in the picture were moving. It didn't look at all like a cinema either; the colours were too real and clean and out-of-door for that. Down went the prow of the ship into the wave and up went a great shock of spray. And then up went the wave behind her, and her stern and her deck became visible for the first time, and then disappeared as the next wave came to meet her and her bows went up again. At the same moment an exercise book which had been lying beside Edmund on the bed flapped, rose and sailed through the air to the wall behind him, and Lucy felt all her hair whipping round her face as it does on a windy day. And this was a windy day; but the wind was blowing out of the picture towards them. And suddenly with the wind came the noises—the swishing of waves and the slap of water against the ship's sides and the creaking and the over-all high, steady roar of air and water. But it was the smell, the wild, briny smell, which really convinced Lucy that she was not dreaming.

"Stop it," came Eustace's voice, squeaky with fright and bad temper. "It's some silly trick you two are playing. Stop it. I'll tell Alberta—ow!"

The other two were much more accustomed to adventures, but, just exactly as Eustace Clarence said "Ow," they both said "Ow" too. The reason was that a great cold, salt splash had broken right out of the frame and they were breathless from the smack of it, besides being wet through.

"I'll smash the rotten thing," cried Eustace; and then several things happened at the same time. Eustace rushed towards the picture. Edmund, who knew something about magic, sprang after him, warning him to look out and not to be a fool. Lucy grabbed at him from the other side and was dragged forward. And by this time either they had grown much smaller or the picture had grown bigger. Eustace jumped to try to pull it off the wall and found himself standing on the frame; in front of him was not glass but real sea, and wind and waves rushing up to the frame as they might to a rock. He lost his head and clutched at the other two who had jumped up beside him. There was a second of struggling and shouting, and just as they thought they had got their balance a great blue roller surged up round them, swept them off their feet, and drew them down into the sea. Eustace's despairing cry suddenly ended as the water got into his mouth.

Lucy thanked her stars that she had worked hard at her swimming last summer term. It is true that she would have got on much better if she had used a slower stroke, and also that the water felt a great deal colder than it had looked while it was only a picture. Still, she kept her head and kicked her shoes off, as everyone ought to do who falls into deep water in their clothes. She even kept her mouth shut and her eyes open. They were still quite near the ship; she saw its green side towering high above them, and people looking at her from the

deck. Then, as one might have expected, Eustace clutched at her in a panic and down they both went.

When they came up again she saw a white figure diving off the ship's side. Edmund was close beside her now, treading water, and had caught the arms of the howling Eustace. Then someone else, whose face was vaguely familiar, slipped an arm under her from the other side. There was a lot of shouting going on from the ship, heads crowding together above the bulwarks, ropes being thrown. Edmund and the stranger were fastening ropes round her. After that followed what seemed a very long delay during which her face got blue and her teeth began chattering. In reality the delay was not very long; they were waiting till the moment when she could be got on board the ship without being dashed against its side. Even with all their best endeavours she had a bruised knee when she finally stood, dripping and shivering, on the deck.

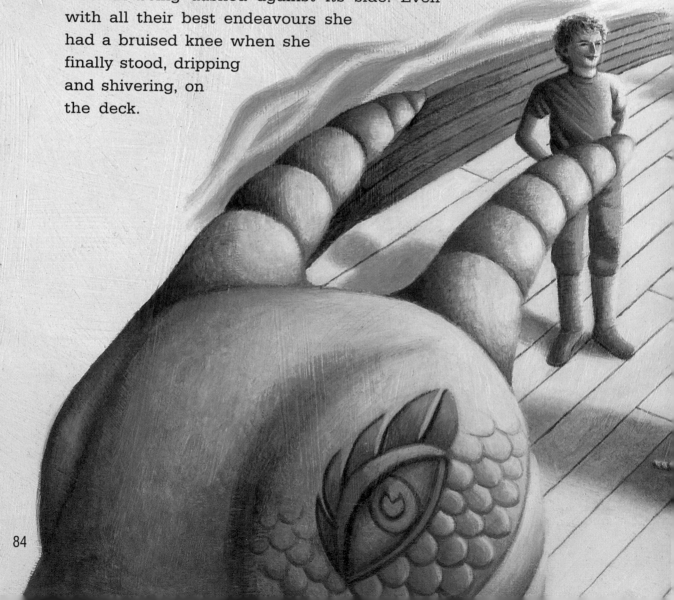

After her Edmund was heaved up, and then the miserable Eustace. Last of all came the stranger—a golden-headed boy some years older than herself.

"Ca—Ca—Caspian!" gasped Lucy as soon as she had breath enough. For Caspian it was; Caspian, the boy king of Narnia whom they had helped to set on the throne during their last visit. Immediately Edmund recognised him too. All three shook hands and clapped one another on the back with great delight.

"But who is your friend?" said Caspian almost at once, turning to Eustace with his cheerful smile. But Eustace was crying much harder than any boy of his age has a right to cry when nothing worse than a wetting has happened to him, and would only yell out, "Let me go. Let me go back. I don't *like* it."

"Let you go?" said Caspian. "But where?"

Eustace rushed to the ship's side, as if he expected to see the picture frame hanging above the sea, and perhaps a glimpse of Lucy's bedroom. What he saw was blue waves flecked with foam, and paler blue sky, both spreading without a break to the horizon. Perhaps we can hardly blame him if his heart sank. He was promptly sick.

"Hey! Rynelf," said Caspian to one of the sailors. "Bring spiced wine for their Majesties. You'll need something to warm you after that dip." He called Edmund and Lucy their Majesties because they and Peter and Susan had all been kings and queens of Narnia long before his time. Narnian time flows differently from ours. If you spent a hundred years in Narnia, you would still come back to our world at the very same hour of the very same day on which you left. And then, if you went back to Narnia after spending a week here, you might find that a thousand Narnian years had passed, or only a day, or no time at all. You never know till you get there. Consequently, when the Pevensie children had returned to Narnia last time for their second visit, it was (for the Narnians) as if King Arthur came back to Britain as some people say he will. And I say the sooner the better.

Rynelf returned with the spiced wine steaming in a flagon and four silver cups. It was just what one wanted, and as Lucy and Edmund sipped it they could feel the warmth going right down to their toes. But Eustace made faces and spluttered and spat it out and was sick again and began to cry again and asked if they hadn't any Plumptree's Vitaminised Nerve Food and could it be made with distilled water and anyway he insisted on being put ashore at the next station.

"This is a merry shipmate you've brought us, Brother," whispered Caspian to Edmund with a chuckle; but before he could say anything more Eustace burst out again.

"Oh! Ugh! What on earth's *that!* Take it away, the horrid thing."

He really had some excuse this time for feeling a little surprised. Something very curious indeed had come out of the cabin in the poop and was slowly approaching them. You might call it—and indeed it was—a Mouse. But then it was a Mouse on its hind legs and stood about two feet high. A thin band of gold passed round its head under one ear and over the other and in this was stuck a long crimson feather. (As the Mouse's fur was very dark, almost black, the effect was bold and striking.) Its left paw rested on the hilt of a sword very nearly as long as its tail. Its balance, as it paced gravely along the swaying deck, was perfect, and its manners courtly. Lucy and Edmund recognised it at once—Reepicheep, the most valiant of all the Talking Beasts of Narnia and the Chief Mouse. It had won undying glory in the second Battle of Beruna. Lucy longed, as she had always done, to take Reepicheep up in her arms and cuddle him. But this, as she well knew, was a pleasure she could never have: it would have offended him deeply. Instead, she went down on one knee to talk to him.

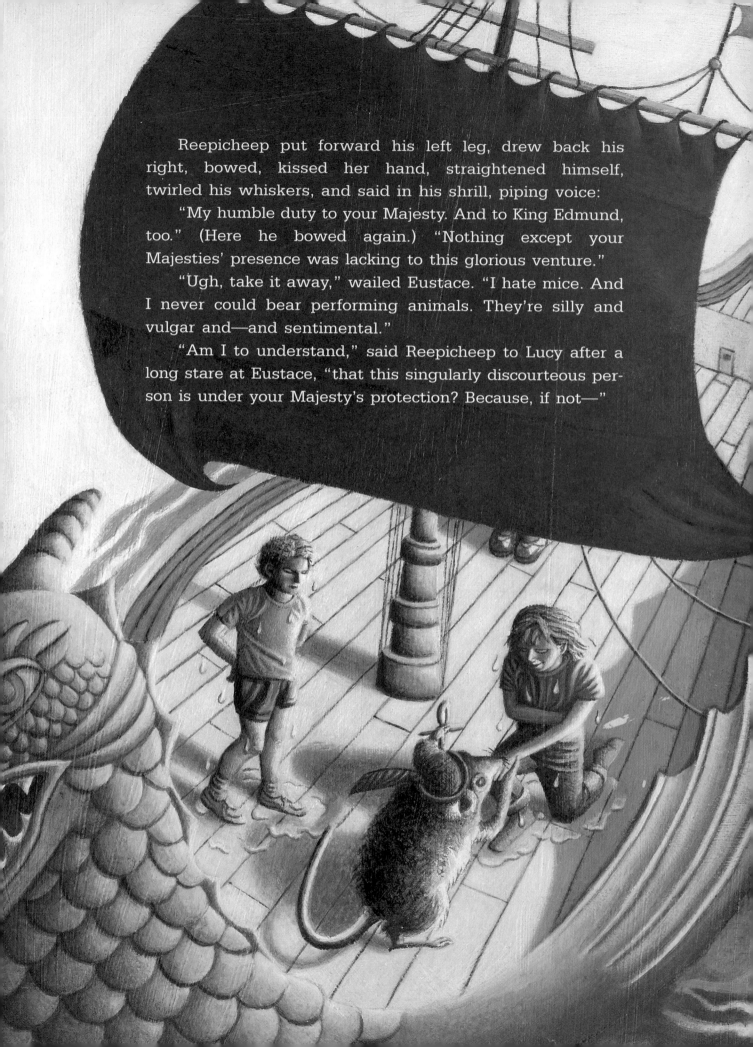

Reepicheep put forward his left leg, drew back his right, bowed, kissed her hand, straightened himself, twirled his whiskers, and said in his shrill, piping voice:

"My humble duty to your Majesty. And to King Edmund, too." (Here he bowed again.) "Nothing except your Majesties' presence was lacking to this glorious venture."

"Ugh, take it away," wailed Eustace. "I hate mice. And I never could bear performing animals. They're silly and vulgar and—and sentimental."

"Am I to understand," said Reepicheep to Lucy after a long stare at Eustace, "that this singularly discourteous person is under your Majesty's protection? Because, if not—"

At this moment Lucy and Edmund both sneezed.

"What a fool I am to keep you all standing here in your wet things," said Caspian. "Come on below and get changed. I'll give you my cabin of course, Lucy, but I'm afraid we have no women's clothes on board. You'll have to make do with some of mine. Lead the way, Reepicheep, like a good fellow."

"To the convenience of a lady," said Reepicheep, "even a question of honour must give way—at least for the moment—" and here he looked very hard at Eustace. But Caspian hustled them on and in a few minutes Lucy found herself passing through the door into the stern cabin. She fell in love with it at once—the three square windows that looked out on the blue, swirling water astern, the low cushioned benches round three sides of the table, the swinging silver lamp overhead (Dwarfs' work, she knew at once by its exquisite delicacy) and the flat gold image of Aslan the Lion on the forward wall above the door. All this she took in in a flash, for Caspian immediately opened a door on the starboard side, and said, "This'll be your room, Lucy. I'll just get some dry things for myself"—he was rummaging in one of the lockers while he spoke—"and then leave you to change. If you'll fling your wet things outside the door I'll get them taken to the galley to be dried."

Lucy found herself as much at home as if she had been in Caspian's cabin for weeks, and the motion of the ship did not worry her, for in the old days when she had been a queen in Narnia she had done a good deal of voyaging. The cabin was very tiny but bright with painted panels (all birds and beasts and crimson dragons and vines) and spotlessly clean. Caspian's clothes were too big for her, but she could manage. His shoes, sandals and sea-boots were hopelessly large but she did not mind going barefoot on board ship. When she had finished dressing she looked out of her window at the water rushing past and took a long deep breath. She felt quite sure they were in for a lovely time.

This is only the beginning of the exciting adventures that Lucy, Edmund, and Eustace experience with their friends in the land of Narnia. You can join them on a voyage of the imagination that leads to magical lands and enchanted happenings when you read the series of books called The Chronicles of Narnia.

Meet
C.S. LEWIS

C. S. Lewis grew up with rows and rows of books in every room of his family's house. These books full of stories spurred his imagination. As a child, he created his own stories of an "Animal-Land" inhabited by dressed animals and knights in armor.

When Lewis grew up, he started writing about the adventures of four brave children in a magic land. He planned just one book, *The Lion, the Witch and the Wardrobe,* but he went on to add six more books to his *Chronicles of Narnia.* In these books, which can be read in any order, the saga of Narnia is told through tales of adventure filled with fantastic creatures.

In *The Magician's Nephew,* Lewis tells how the passage between earth and Narnia was created: A tree grown from the magical Narnia apple blew over, and its wood was used to build a wardrobe. Through this wardrobe, the children first enter Narnia, where they help the lord-lion Aslan fight the powers of evil.

Lewis advised one young girl who had written to him, "Write about what really interests you, whether it is real or imaginary things." Following his own advice, Lewis created an entire world for readers.

maggie and milly and molly and may
went down to the beach(to play one day)

and maggie discovered a shell that sang
so sweetly she couldn't remember her troubles,and

milly befriended a stranded star
whose rays five languid fingers were;

and molly was chased by a horrible thing
which raced sideways while blowing bubbles:and

may came home with a smooth round stone
as small as a world and as large as alone.

For whatever we lose(like a you or a me)
it's always ourselves we find in the sea

e. e. cummings

by Elizabeth Tayntor, Paul Erickson, and Les Kaufman

DIVE
TO THE
CORAL
REEFS

A NEW ENGLAND AQUARIUM BOOK

Did you know that there is a city full of fantastic shapes and structures that lies beneath the surface of the sea? It is a city few people have seen because it is so difficult to reach.

Yet it is one of the largest, most colorful, most amazing communities in the world. It is built and inhabited by millions of incredible creatures. It is the living coral reef.

Coral reefs grow in tropical oceans all over the world. The largest, over 1,200 miles long, is the Great Barrier Reef off the coast of Australia. To find out about these underwater coral communities, the New England Aquarium sent a team of scientists and divers to the island of Jamaica in the Caribbean Sea. Their mission: to explore the legendary Pear Tree and Rio Bueno reefs off the island's north coast.

Down here, the coral grows nearly the whole length of the island, from east to west. It rises 40 feet above the sea floor. The divers explored reef growth more than 5,000 years old.

Reefs are built very, very slowly, by corals: tiny animals that actually make up the mounds, boulders, and branches called a coral reef. For example, a mound of brain coral, 3 feet tall, may be 250 years old.

Each coral animal, or polyp, is about the size of a pencil eraser.

A coral polyp has a soft body, stomach, and mouth surrounded by tentacles. Corals are hunters. Like their cousins, the jellyfishes, they use their tentacles to capture their prey, small drifting plants and animals called plankton.

Some people are surprised to find out that corals are animals because many look more like plants. There is something amazing about corals that helps to explain their plantlike shapes. Scientists have discovered that coral animals are also part plant.

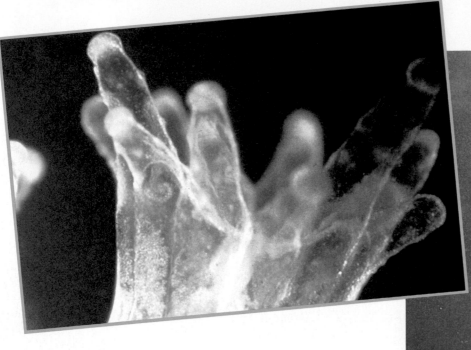

Imagine tiny green plants growing under your skin. Corals have tiny plants, called zooxanthellae, growing inside of them. Like other plants, zooxanthellae use the sun to make food through a process called photosynthesis. Then they pass some of this food on to the coral polyps, and this helps the coral grow.

Each coral polyp uses minerals from seawater to build a limestone skeleton. When disturbed, polyps can pull into the protection of these hard, rocklike homes.

When we think of coral, we often picture the hard white skeletons of corals that have died. Polyps, like people, live close together in colonies. As polyps grow, they move up to build new skeletons on top of the old. And, very slowly, the reef grows with them. It's like a modern city built upon the ruins of an ancient civilization.

Hundreds of individuals make up the forms of the reef. Different species of coral form different shapes.

Staghorn coral looks like deer antlers.

You can see how plate coral gets its name. It is big and flat, like a giant dinner plate.

Brain coral looks like the surface of a human brain with furrows and ridges.

These corals build hard skeletons. . . .

But sea fans, sea whips, and other soft corals have flexible skeletons. In ocean currents, soft corals bend and sway like tree branches in a heavy breeze.

The reef is home to literally millions of plants and animals because it offers good feeding and good places to hide. Small reef
dwellers need protection from the many hunters of the reef.

Larger fishes probe cracks and holes in the reef, looking for
tasty crabs and worms.

Butterflyfishes are especially good at this because they have
long snouts and they can reach into places other fishes can't.

But in no time at all, the tables can turn and hunters become the hunted, victims of larger predators like the great barracuda (left). This fish grows to 6 feet in length and attacks its prey with lightning speed.

The great barracuda was curious about the divers, following them for a long time. But despite its curiosity, the big fish is not likely to attack snorkelers and divers.

The reef is a feeding ground for a variety of sharks. This white-tipped shark (above) has 7 rows of sharp teeth for hunting. When a tooth from the front row falls out, one from behind moves up to take its place. Though sharks do not hunt people for food, divers are cautious and give them plenty of room.

As they snorkeled over the reef, the divers saw nurse sharks resting on the sand. Nurse sharks feed on spiny lobsters and crabs. They act like underwater vacuum cleaners. They move close to a hole and suck their victims right out of hiding places in the reef.

The divers surprised a sea turtle who was sleeping under a ledge. Like humans, sea turtles need to come up for air. But unlike people, these turtles can hold their breath for up to 2 hours.

Animals and plants are everywhere on the reef. Every inch of space is used by living things. Some animals even live inside other animals: shrimp in sponges, and worms in coral.

These snapping shrimp are just two of dozens that were living inside a sponge. To defend itself, the shrimp uses its large claw to make a loud snapping sound that startles nearby hungry predators.

Exploring the shallow reef was just one part of the New England Aquarium dive team's job. Next they dove the deep reef. The divers dropped off the reef edge and descended 100 feet down the reef wall. Special training is required to make a dive like this and it challenges even experts!

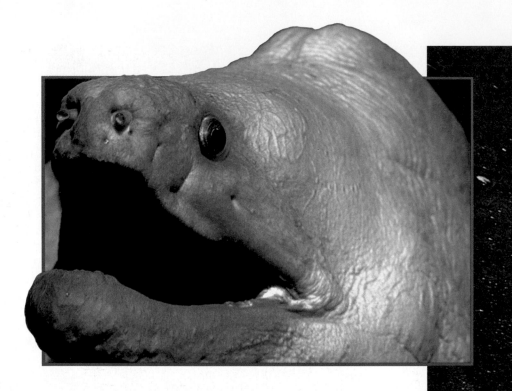

One of the divers describes how it feels to dive the deep reef: "Diving the reef wall is like flying off the side of a mountain with a thousand feet of open water below you."

As the divers went deeper, it got darker.

At about 60 feet, they looked into a crack in the reef, and an octopus came shooting out and draped itself over the corals. Frightened, the octopus changed colors. These camouflage experts are shy animals and it is rare to see one in the open.

At 80 feet down the divers entered a long cave . . . and came out 100 feet below the water's surface.

Here it feels like being on another planet. Enormous sponges grow out of the reef wall. Some are so large a diver can stand inside.

A green moray eel stared out from its underwater cave. By day these fish hide, waiting for something to come a little bit too close. Then they lunge out at it with their sharp teeth. At night they may hunt for octopus and lobsters.

The divers were amazed by the beauty of the reef and the number of organisms that live there. Because everything fits together like a puzzle, one change can create problems for everyone.

In the coral reefs, natural as well as human disasters cause destruction. Dense thickets of staghorn coral are often victims of hurricanes. Despite their hard skeletons, stony corals are surprisingly fragile and easily damaged by anchor-dragging boats. Souvenir collectors destroy living coral that may be decades old.

Probably the greatest threat to corals is coastline development. Offshore oil spills and open ocean dumping may destroy large areas of the reef forever.

Coral reefs can only be preserved through wise ocean management. So maybe someday you, too, can put on scuba tanks and explore this fantastic underwater world.

MEET
LES KAUFMAN,
ELIZABETH TAYNTOR,
and PAUL ERICKSON

Les Kaufman can't remember a time when he wasn't interested in nature and science. A few years ago, when Kaufman headed the New England Aquarium's education department, a new 186,000-gallon exhibit showing a coral reef in the Caribbean Sea was developed. Kaufman worked with his fellow Aquarium staff members Elizabeth Tayntor and Paul Erickson to create a filmstrip that led the three to write *Dive to the Coral Reefs*. The authors wrote the book to help young people gain a sense of the wonder of nature and the value of understanding it.

Kaufman sees science as a tool for understanding nature. "All the horrible things kids are hearing about the world falling apart ecologically are true. What they are not hearing is that these things can be fixed. We've got to clean up about 20 thousand years of damage. We've made a start. It will be up to the kids to continue the work." Kaufman thinks that even if kids who go into marine biology don't solve all the problems, they'll get another kind of payoff: coming to know nature as few people do. Kaufman promises, "The reward is enormous."

Fellow divers and authors Elizabeth Tayntor and Paul Erickson

113

SCUBA DIVING

The silence of diving.
Slipping through
the water like a
worm sliding
through mud.
Skittering along
the bottom of the
ocean floor like a
hamster.
A big whale flies by like a silent jet.
Giant coral reefs like big
skyscrapers in the sea.
Bubbles coming from a rubber tube
like smoke coming from a factory.
Giant fish floating by like a
submarine.
Giant flippers propelling you further
and further into the ocean.

Stuart Francis, Grade 6
Widsten Elementary School
Wayzata, Minnesota

CONTENTS

TRANSFORMATIONS

Nothing is permanent but change.

HERACLITUS
500 B.C.

New Pro

vidence

a changing cityscape

by Renata
von Tscharner
and Ronald
Lee Fleming

illustrated by Denis Orloff

1910

Put the city up; tear the city down;
put it up again; let us find a city....

—Carl Sandburg

New Providence is thriving. Cobblestone streets bustle with activity—Model T Fords, streetcars, and horse-drawn carts carrying meat, milk, and ice. There is no concert in the band-stand today, but a crowd has gathered in the square in front of the Town Hall and the Tenebo County Courthouse. A fountain has been built in commemoration of Chief Tenebo, a Native American from a local tribe. The statue is about to be unveiled. Around the

base of the fountain is an inscription: GOOD CITIZENS ARE THE RICHES OF A CITY.

New Providence's good citizens—women in long skirts and men in hats—buy fruit at the sidewalk stand in front of the grocery and most of their clothing and household items at Getz & McClure's, the largest store in town. They shop for shoes and jewelry and office supplies and have supper at Gilman's or at the Butler House Cafe.

The rural hillsides surrounding the city are lush, with comfortable Victorian homes dotting the landscape and the Bloom mill and worker housing in the distance. The large red brick schoolhouse is attended by all school-age children in the region. A flock of birds flies peacefully overhead.

1935

As a mist rolls into New Providence, effects of the Great Depression are visible; the city has fallen on hard times. Gone is the bandstand from the courthouse square, where homeless men now huddle over trash can fires for warmth. A WPA sign publicizes the Works Progress Administration, a jobs program funded by the government. A line of jobless men waits for free bread outside the post office, and hoboes are taking a free ride out of the city on trains. Many buildings are in need of repair.

But even in times such as these, life goes on. A Charlie Chaplin movie is playing at the Strand Theater. A huge Coca-Cola advertisement goes up on the side of a building. A street-light now controls automobile traffic. The Bloom mill—expanded before the stock market crash—is still in operation, the grocery has become a shoe store, and the dry goods store, a jeweler's. The Colonel Fleming House now accommodates three small businesses. Art Deco chrome and glass streamline some of the storefronts, contrasting with the older styles of the upper stories. A modern yellow apartment building squats on the hillside, while a biplane and a blimp cruise the skies.

1955

A postwar prosperity settles over New Providence, although there are signs that downtown is deteriorating.

The night sky glows with neon, Christmas lights, and lighted billboards advertising bread, used cars, and cigarettes. Part of the courthouse square is now paved with asphalt to make room for more and larger cars. Buses have replaced streetcars. Franchises like Rexall's and Woolworth's have moved into town, and the Alpine Motel attracts traveling businessmen. Walt Disney's *Lady and the Tramp* is playing at the Strand.

The elegant Butler House is now a liquor store and a boarding house for transients. Next to it, a Victorian cast-iron building is being covered with prefabricated siding. Getz & McClure's has already been sheathed with stark metal grillwork and a currently popular style of lettering. Two of the small businesses in the Colonel Fleming House are boarded up. Behind it, a bland new building has been erected to house Monarch Insurance. The old slate roof of the Town Hall has been replaced by asphalt shingles. A fire is raging at the train station, while the citizens of New Providence go about their holiday shopping.

1970

By 1970, downtown New Providence is an uninspired jumble of old and new. To attract people from thriving suburbia, part of Main Street has been converted into a pedestrian mall, dominated by a harsh concrete fountain. But there is less traffic than ever in the city center, and fewer people actually live there.

A number of people in town today are gathered outside the courthouse, taking part in a protest march against the Vietnam War. Across the newly sunken and cemented square, a mugging is in progress. Graffiti mars the area, as do more and more billboards—advertising beer, cigarettes, whiskey, and an Army/Navy surplus

store. The post office and several other buildings have been demolished and turned into parking lots, the Bloom mill is for rent, and the train station tower remains burnt out.

The Alpine Motel is now a Holiday Inn, a Fotomat has opened, and the Beatles' *Let It Be* is playing at the Strand. A day school has opened, complete with colorful murals and giant toadstools. The Colonel Fleming House seems about to be rescued by a preservation group. Victorian homes in the hills are disappearing to make room for highways, look-alike suburban housing, and another addition to the school. In the afternoon sky, a jet flies over the increasing number of powerlines strung across the horizon.

129

1980

*T*en years later, there are signs that downtown New Providence is sadly in need of recovery—and also signs that help is on the way.

Chief Tenebo's statue has been vandalized; debris blows around its dry base and across the square. Graffiti is everywhere, street lamps are smashed, and a police box has appeared. The Colonel Fleming House has been moved across the street, but its placement does not look permanent. In its old location are a Cor-Ten steel sculpture and Monarch Insurance's new highrise, which bears no architectural relationship to the buildings around it.

But the streets seem more populated, and people are again living—even barbecuing—downtown in the new red brick infill structure next to McDonald's. The only billboard in town advertises health food and a cultural event. The old Strand Theater is being expanded into a Cultural Center. And although the Butler House has been all but abandoned, a sign shows that rehabilitation is being planned. A superhighway now cuts through the hillside, making downtown more accessible to summer holiday travelers. A large parking structure has been built, and well-tended plantings soften the mall.

1987

It is wisdom to think the people are the city. . . .
—Carl Sandburg

In the sunny afternoon sky a flock of birds heads back to its winter home. Below, people have returned to the city—living, shopping, working, playing. New Providence has never looked better. Sidewalk vendors sell their produce once more, and traffic again flows through handsomely paved streets. Buses are made to look like old-fashioned trolleys. Chief Tenebo has been restored, and the bandstand is back, a concert in full swing. Gone are graffiti, billboards, and harsh sculptures. Plants and fall flowers are everywhere—even the parking structure has been elegantly camouflaged.

All of the old building facades have been renovated, and the condition of most buildings is strikingly similar to what it was in 1910. The Town Hall's slate roof has been restored, and the air-raid siren is gone. Street furniture is comfortable and compatible with the architecture. The circular clock is back in front of the Butler House, now beautifully refurbished. An arcaded building where people live and work occupies the site of the controversial tower, serving as an entry into the restored train station, and an atrium full of plants softens the Monarch Insurance skyscraper. A Fitness Center has replaced the Feminist Health Center, and a film festival is in progress at the Strand Cultural Center.

The good citizens of New Providence have worked hard to make the city livable again—and true to its heritage.

*N*ew Providence, a small American city, will not be found on any map. It is the creation of a team of architectural historians and designers, and yet its fictional cityscape is truly authentic. The buildings, the signs, even the street furniture can be found somewhere in urban America. Almost every detail was discovered in old photographs and assembled by the design team at The Townscape Institute.

Baltimore, Maryland
(McDonald's building and H_2O fountain)

Binghamton, New York
(courthouse lights)

Boston, Massachusetts
(church in center and 1970 concrete plaza)

Brookline, Massachusetts
(church)

Cambridge, Massachusetts
(signs)

Chelsea, Massachusetts
(storefront)

Chicago, Illinois
(metal awning on the Butler House)

Cincinnati, Ohio
(1987 City Identity System booth)

Denver, Colorado
(building across the street from courthouse in 1910)

Eugene, Oregon
(1970 modern concrete fountain)

Flint, Michigan
(1910 shoe sign and street awnings)

Fresno, California
(1970-80 sculptural clock tower)

Garland, Utah
(Bloom mill)

Grand Rapids, Michigan
(City Hall)

Heber City, Utah
(water tower)

Junction City, Kansas
(corner bank)

Knoxville, Tennessee
(billboard)

Los Angeles, California
(Getz & McClure building)

Milwaukee, Wisconsin
(suburban villas)

Montclair, New Jersey
(Colonel Fleming House)

Montgomery, Alabama
(Victorian cast-iron building)

New York, New York
(Butler House and train station)

Portland, Oregon
(fountain base)

Richmond, Virginia
(signs on Reiter's shoe store)

Salem, Ohio
(cornice on Main Street)

San Diego, California
(circular clock)

Scottsdale, Arizona
(parking structure with plantings)

Staunton, Virginia
(stained glass in McDonald's building)

Syracuse, New York
(layout of courthouse square)

Topeka, Kansas
(Alpine Motel sign)

Townsend, Massachusetts
(bandstand)

Traverse City, Michigan
(mansard roof on Butler House)

Upper Sandusky, Ohio
(horse fountain and pavilion)

Waltham, Massachusetts
(bench)

Washington, D.C.
(Masonic building)

Westerville, Ohio
(gas station)

Wilkes-Barre, Pennsylvania
(park outline)

Wilmington, Delaware
(1970 metal Main Street shelters)

Winooski, Vermont
(Main Street building)

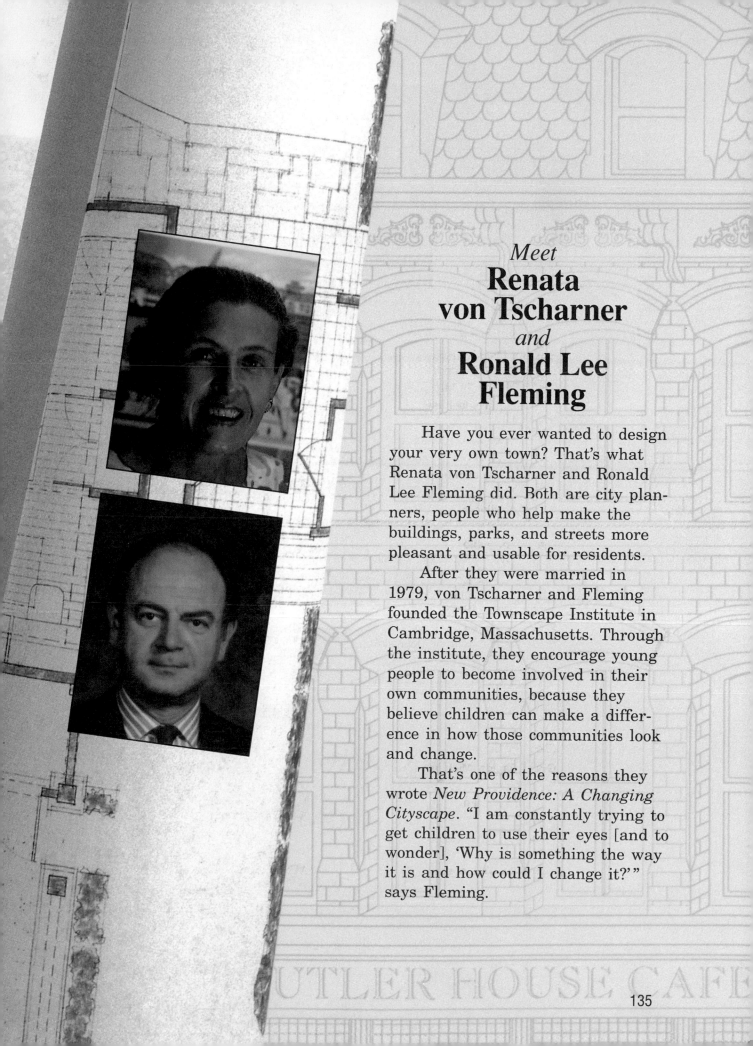

Meet
Renata
von Tscharner
and
Ronald Lee
Fleming

Have you ever wanted to design your very own town? That's what Renata von Tscharner and Ronald Lee Fleming did. Both are city planners, people who help make the buildings, parks, and streets more pleasant and usable for residents.

After they were married in 1979, von Tscharner and Fleming founded the Townscape Institute in Cambridge, Massachusetts. Through the institute, they encourage young people to become involved in their own communities, because they believe children can make a difference in how those communities look and change.

That's one of the reasons they wrote *New Providence: A Changing Cityscape.* "I am constantly trying to get children to use their eyes [and to wonder], 'Why is something the way it is and how could I change it?'" says Fleming.

135

CITY

In the morning the city
Spreads its wings
Making a song
In stone that sings.

In the evening the city
Goes to bed
Hanging lights
About its head.

Langston Hughes

Be An Inventor

by Barbara Taylor

☆Where do inventions come from?☆

☆How does an inventor transform an idea into reality?☆

A Behind-the-Scenes Look at Some Inventions

Have you ever asked yourself, "Why didn't I think of that?" when you've seen an invention you liked?

Why does one person think of the idea for an invention before anyone else does?

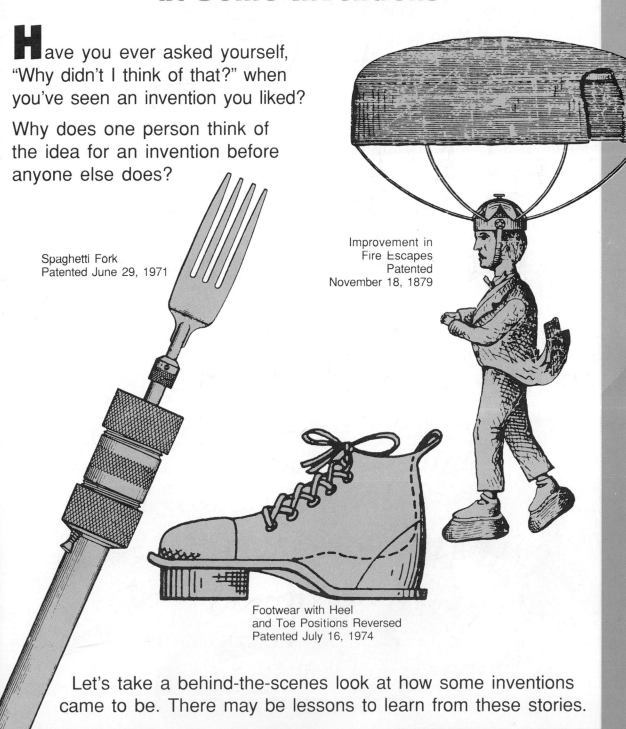

Spaghetti Fork
Patented June 29, 1971

Improvement in
Fire Escapes
Patented
November 18, 1879

Footwear with Heel
and Toe Positions Reversed
Patented July 16, 1974

Let's take a behind-the-scenes look at how some inventions came to be. There may be lessons to learn from these stories.

Something to Keep the Ears Warm

Some inventors invent things *that they themselves need.* Then they discover, often to their surprise, that other people need their invention, too.

Fifteen-year-old Chester Greenwood of Farmington, Maine, had a problem with his ears. They were very sensitive to the freezing cold of the long Maine winters.

While other children his age would race sleds down slopes, build ice forts, and skate on frozen ponds, poor Chester would rub his ears and go home.

One December day in 1873, Chester decided he had to do something. He tied a scarf around his head, but it itched and would not stay in place. Then he hit upon the idea of covering just his ears. Chester bent a piece of wire into loops, fitted the loops over his ears, and attached the loops to a hat. Chester asked his grandmother to cover them with wool and fur.

When the other kids saw Chester in his strange headgear, they laughed. But the laughter stopped when they realized that Chester was staying outside in the cold longer than he ever had before. Soon the other kids were asking Chester if he would make them covers for their ears. Chester Greenwood realized he was on to something big.

Orders from all over town started pouring in. Chester's mom and grandmother were busy helping him make more earmuffs, the name people were calling Greenwood's clever invention.

As word of Chester's earmuffs spread throughout New England, the inventor found ways to improve his invention. Instead of attaching the ear covers to a hat, Chester fastened them to the end of a strip of flat metal that he fitted over his head. The band held the ear covers firmly in place.

By the time he was 19, Chester had received a patent for his invention and was well on his way to becoming rich and successful. To keep up with all the orders, he designed machines to manufacture the earmuffs, and set up a factory right in Farmington. Although he went on to produce many other inventions, Chester continued to operate his earmuff factory until his death in 1937.

Today Farmington, Maine, is known as "the earmuff capital of the world." Every year on December 21, the first day of winter, Farmington celebrates "Chester Greenwood Day" to honor a clever boy who found a way to keep his ears—and millions of other ears—warm.

These early ads show the inventor of earmuffs proudly promoting his product. Chester Greenwood's imagination served him well all of his life. He is credited with more than 100 other inventions.

Greenwood's Ear Protectors

Worn by Millions

25c

"Blizzard Proof"

Hero of the Safety Hood

Some people create inventions that make life safer for others. They get their ideas by thinking of other people's welfare instead of their own needs or comforts.

Garrett Morgan was granted a patent in 1912 for the Morgan Safety Hood, a special breathing helmet that pumped air directly into a mask that fitted over a person's face. The air was stored in a bag attached to the mask. There was enough air in the bag for 15 to 20 minutes of breathing—enough time for a firefighter to enter a smoke-filled burning building and rescue people inside.

Morgan was awarded the grand prize at the Industrial Exposition of Safety in New York in 1914, but it wasn't until an unexpected disaster in 1916 that Morgan and his invention became famous.

One night a tunnel collapsed 250 feet below the surface of Lake Erie in Morgan's hometown of Cleveland, Ohio. Workers from the Cleveland Waterworks were overcome by deadly gas fumes and trapped in the tunnel.

First three-way traffic signal
Garrett Morgan, pioneer in safety

Poisonous gas drove back firefighters who tried to reach the trapped men. But someone at the scene of the disaster remembered seeing Morgan give a demonstration of his safety hood some weeks before.

Police quickly located the inventor and asked him to come to their aid. Morgan, accompanied by his brother, arrived at the scene of the disaster with safety hoods. The two entered the clouded tunnel to rescue the helpless workers inside.

Morgan and his brother succeeded in carrying all 32 trapped workmen from the tunnel. Fortunately, many were still alive and the inventor was proclaimed a hero. As news spread of the daring rescue, his safety hood became a great success. Soon it was standard equipment in fire departments across the nation.

When the United States entered World War I, Morgan adapted his safety hood into a gas mask that was worn by American soldiers fighting in Europe. The masks protected them from deadly chlorine fumes on the battlefield.

Garrett Morgan continued to invent, keeping other people's welfare in mind. He designed the first three-way traffic signal, making roadways safer for millions of motorists. Before he died in 1963 at the age of 86, Garrett Morgan had lived to see the United States a safer country, thanks to his inventions.

The Fabulous Frisbee

Some inventors take a common item already in existence and find an entirely new use for it. That's how the popular toy the Frisbee came to be.

One day in 1948, Walter Fred Morrison happened to be driving past the Frisbie Pie Company in Bridgeport, Connecticut, when he saw two truck drivers tossing empty pie pans back and forth in the parking lot.

It reminded Morrison of his childhood, when he'd thrown pie pans with his playmates. Returning home to Los Angeles, California, Morrison went to work designing a disc that could be thrown back and forth like the pie pans. The disc had to be light enough not to hurt someone who got in its flight path and still heavy enough to fly a good distance. He found the right material for his toy—a soft plastic that was bouncy but tough. He called his invention "Morrison's Flyin' Saucer" and took two cartons of his toys to a nearby county fair to sell.

Morrison thought of a gimmick to make people want to buy his flying saucers. He told the crowds at the fair that there was an "invisible wire" stretched between him and a friend. When Morrison threw the saucer, he claimed it flew along the wire directly to his friend's waiting hand. Morrison charged one cent per foot for the invisible wire and threw in a "free" Flyin' Saucer with every 100 feet of wire a customer bought. The gimmick worked and soon Morrison had sold out his supply of saucers and invisible wire.

But Morrison still wasn't satisfied. He improved the design and gave the toy a new name—the Pluto Platter. In 1957, the Wham-O Toy Company of San Gabriel, California, saw the Pluto Platter, liked it, and bought it from Morrison.

Sales of Pluto Platters were steady among beachgoers who loved playing catch with them, but were slow among the general public. Then one day, Wham-O owner Rich Knerr saw some college students throwing the Platters at Harvard University in Cambridge, Massachusetts. The students told him how they used to throw pie pans from the Frisbie Pie Company. Knerr remembered Morrison's story about the same pie company and decided that a change of name would make the toy more popular. The Pluto Platter became the Frisbee (an unintentional misspelling) and the rest is history.

The Frisbee remains popular with people of all ages and athletic abilities. And it all started with an empty pie pan and an inventor with imagination.

Introducing *Weekly Reader's* Young Inventors

Weekly Reader, *the classroom newspaper, has recently sponsored national invention contests. More than 300,000 students entered the contests. Here are some of the contestants and their ideas—dramatic evidence that young people can think up amazing and useful inventions.*

Katie Harding, a kindergartner, invented the **Mudpuddle-Spotter**—*an umbrella with a flashlight attached to the handle. It helps her avoid puddles while walking along her driveway after dark.*

First-grader Suzie Amling (left) won a grand prize for her **Line Leader and Keeper.** *Suzie's invention helps her teacher keep students in line as they walk along a busy street to the library. Suzie designed a rope with handles for each child. If a child lets go of a handle, a box at the teacher's end of the rope beeps a warning.*

Jim Wollin, an eighth-grader, invented the clever **Jar of Plenty** to help people get to the bottom of food jars. Jim's jar has a lid at both ends, so reaching all the food in the jar is easy.

Seventh-grader Clint Vaught won a grand prize for his **Logg Hogg Lifting Arm.** The invention helps Clint split heavy logs when his dad's not around. It lifts the logs onto a log splitter that cuts them into suitable sizes for the Vaughts' stove.

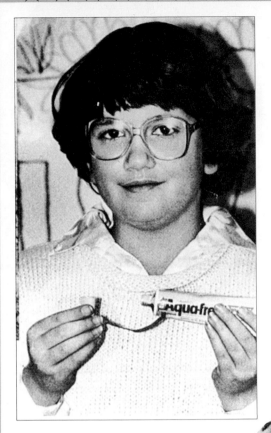

Kim Mehuron, a third-grader, invented the **Jim Dandy Unlosable Toothpaste Cap** to prevent the cap from going down the drain. The cap is permanently attached to the tube of toothpaste with a rubber band.

Fifth-grader Chris Robben's baby brother chewed on the germ-ridden handles of shopping carts at the supermarket. So Chris cut a plastic shower-rod cover that fits over the shopping cart handle. He calls it the **Germ Buster.** Now his brother can chew to his heart's content and not get sick.

Second-grader Ryan Johnson won a prize for his **Keep-Warm Bird Feeder.** Ryan's mom was cold when she went outside to feed the birds each morning, so Ryan came up with a way to do the job without leaving the house. He cut a small door in the wall of his home. The door opens into the outside bird feeder.

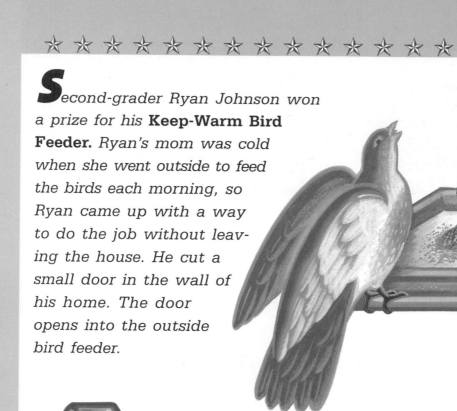

Fourth-grader Jennifer Acosta came up with a **Pop Top Mouthpiece.** Jennifer's reusable mouthpiece snaps into the slot where the top was pulled off a not-so-clean can and allows the user to drink without fear of germs.

Kindergartner Daniel Randall solved the problem of dangling shoelaces with his **Shoe Magnet.** He thought of metal tips for shoelaces that cling to magnets on the shoes and keep the laces out of the way.

Jennifer Horowitz, a fifth-grader, sat at the corner of her dinner table where the table leg always got in her way. So Jenny invented the **Special Corner Chair.** It has a groove cut into the seat so that Jenny can pull right up to the table leg and straddle it.

Sixth-grader Scott Burnett invented his **School Bus Early Warning System** so he can wait for the school bus inside his home when the weather is bad. Scott's invention picks up a signal from the bus on an FM radio while he sits safe and dry inside.

HERE COMES THE BUS

Suzanna Goodin, a first-grader, won a grand prize for creating the first **Edible Pet Food Server.** She got the idea for the invention because she was tired of washing spoons after she fed her kittens. The server is a cracker in the shape of a spoon that a pet can eat as part of its dinner after the "spoon" has been used to serve pet food.

Eighth-grader Danielle Dorsey invented the **Clutch Crutch Cap** to help a person on crutches walk safely over ice and snow. The cap fits over the end of a crutch. It has sharp spikes that crack through the ice and support the person securely.

Mark Mueller was tired of soggy cereal. So the fourth-grader invented the **Cereal Plate**—a bowl with an angled bottom that keeps the cereal and the milk separate until they are mixed together.

Third-grader April Baque's baby brother cried every time his mom used cold wipes at diaper-changing time. Now he's all smiles since April invented the **Baby Wipes Warmer**—a box that plugs into an electrical outlet to heat the wipes.

Third-grader Charlie Gurganus invented his **Bowling Ball** to speed up a bowling game. Bowlers don't have to waste time looking for the finger holes because the ball is covered with them.

Second-grader Eric Vendura invented his **Sleeve Stopper** to help people put on coats without bunching up their sleeves. Eric's invention is a loop of elastic that is attached to each shirt or sweater sleeve. A person hooks a thumb into each loop before putting on his or her coat.

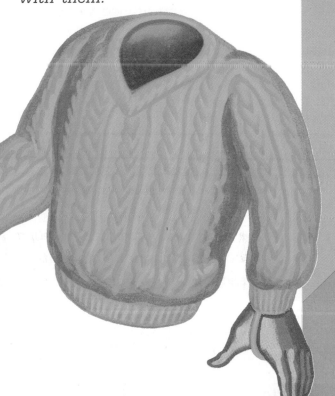

Alex Nicander didn't have much use for his seesaw when his playmates weren't around. So the third-grader invented the **Seesaw Spring** that fits under the empty seat. Now Alex can seesaw all by himself.

Epilogue

Do you have an idea for an invention? There are inventors' groups that offer seminars, newsletters, and advice to help you get started.

American Society of Inventors, 23 Palisades Avenue, Absecon, NJ 08207

Midwestern Inventors Society, P.O. Box 335, St. Cloud, MN 56301

National Congress of Inventor Organizations, P.O. Box 158, Rheem Valley, CA 94570

MEET
BARBARA TAYLOR

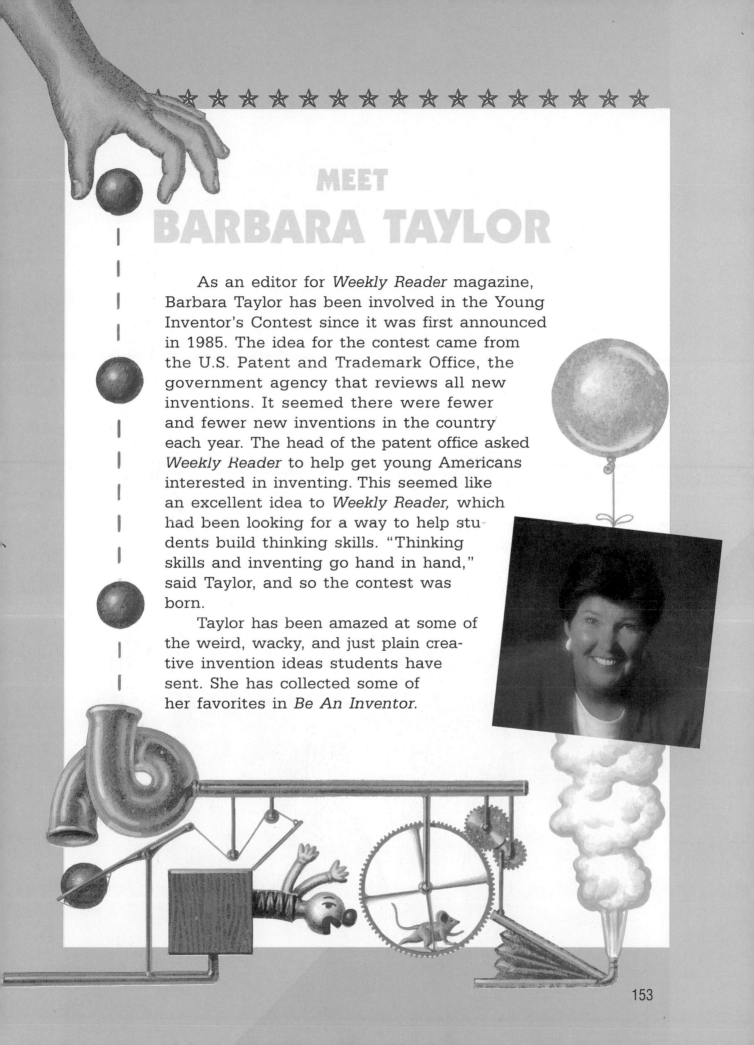

As an editor for *Weekly Reader* magazine, Barbara Taylor has been involved in the Young Inventor's Contest since it was first announced in 1985. The idea for the contest came from the U.S. Patent and Trademark Office, the government agency that reviews all new inventions. It seemed there were fewer and fewer new inventions in the country each year. The head of the patent office asked *Weekly Reader* to help get young Americans interested in inventing. This seemed like an excellent idea to *Weekly Reader,* which had been looking for a way to help students build thinking skills. "Thinking skills and inventing go hand in hand," said Taylor, and so the contest was born.

Taylor has been amazed at some of the weird, wacky, and just plain creative invention ideas students have sent. She has collected some of her favorites in *Be An Inventor.*

Imagination

154

Imagination is a new idea beginning to grow
In the warm, soft earth of all we know.

Mary O'Neill

YOU'LL NEVER

Insect Metamorphosis
by Ron and Nancy Goor
Atheneum, 1990

Buffalo Woman
by Paul Goble
Aladdin, 1986

BE THE SAME

Meet
Alma Flor Ada

"Most of my stories I told aloud before I ever wrote them down," says Alma Flor Ada. "And it was other people listening and other people being interested that gave me a motivation to write them."

Listening to other people's stories has also influenced Ada's writing. *The Gold Coin* is based in part on a story her grandfather told her when she was about fifteen. In the story, a rich man had to choose between going away to save his fortune or staying with his dying wife. That man was Alma Flor Ada's grandfather—and he told her he never regretted choosing to stay with his wife. "[Money] should never rule your life," he told her.

Alma Flor Ada grew up in Cuba and today lives in California, where she is a professor of multicultural education at the University of San Francisco. She has written many children's books published in Mexico, Peru, Argentina, and Spain.

THE GOLD COIN

by Alma Flor Ada

illustrated by Neil Waldman

translated from the Spanish by Bernice Randall

Juan had been a thief for many years. Because he did his stealing by night, his skin had become pale and sickly. Because he spent his time either hiding or sneaking about, his body had become shriveled and bent. And because he had neither friend nor relative to make him smile, his face was always twisted into an angry frown.

One night, drawn by a light shining through the trees, Juan came upon a hut. He crept up to the door and through a crack saw an old woman sitting at a plain, wooden table.

What was that shining in her hand? Juan wondered. He could not believe his eyes: It was a gold coin. Then he heard the woman say to herself, "I must be the richest person in the world."

Juan decided instantly that all the woman's gold must be his. He thought that the easiest thing to do was to watch until the woman left. Juan hid in the bushes and huddled under his poncho, waiting for the right moment to enter the hut.

Juan was half asleep when he heard knocking at the door and the sound of insistent voices. A few minutes later, he saw the woman, wrapped in a black cloak, leave the hut with two men at her side.

Here's my chance! Juan thought. And, forcing open a window, he climbed into the empty hut.

He looked about eagerly for the gold. He looked under the bed. It wasn't there. He looked in the cupboard. It wasn't there, either. Where could it be? Close to despair, Juan tore away some beams supporting the thatch roof.

Finally, he gave up. There was simply no gold in the hut.

All I can do, he thought, is to find the old woman and make her tell me where she's hidden it.

So he set out along the path that she and her two companions had taken.

It was daylight by the time Juan reached the river. The countryside had been deserted, but here, along the riverbank, were two huts. Nearby, a man and his son were hard at work, hoeing potatoes.

It had been a long, long time since Juan had spoken to another human being. Yet his desire to find the woman was so strong that he went up to the farmers and asked, in a hoarse, raspy voice, "Have you seen a short, gray-haired woman, wearing a black cloak?"

"Oh, you must be looking for Doña Josefa," the young boy said. "Yes, we've seen her. We went to fetch her this morning, because my grandfather had another attack of—"

"Where is she now?" Juan broke in.

"She is long gone," said the father with a smile. "Some people from across the river came looking for her, because someone in their family is sick."

"How can I get across the river?" Juan asked anxiously.

"Only by boat," the boy answered. "We'll row you across later, if you'd like." Then turning back to his work, he added, "But first we must finish digging up the potatoes."

The thief muttered, "Thanks." But he quickly grew impatient. He grabbed a hoe and began to help the pair of farmers. The sooner we finish, the sooner we'll get across the river, he thought. And the sooner I'll get to my gold!

It was dusk when they finally laid down their hoes. The soil had been turned, and the wicker baskets were brimming with potatoes.

"Now can you row me across?" Juan asked the father anxiously.

"Certainly," the man said. "But let's eat supper first."

Juan had forgotten the taste of a home-cooked meal and the pleasure that comes from sharing it with others. As he sopped up the last of the stew with a chunk of dark bread, memories of other meals came back to him from far away and long ago.

By the light of the moon, father and son guided their boat across the river.

"What a wonderful healer Doña Josefa is!" the boy told Juan. "All she had to do to make Abuelo better was give him a cup of her special tea."

"Yes, and not only that," his father added, "she brought him a gold coin."

Juan was stunned. It was one thing for Doña Josefa to go around helping people. But how could she go around handing out gold coins—*his gold coins?*

When the threesome finally reached the other side of the river, they saw a young man sitting outside his hut.

"This fellow is looking for Doña Josefa," the father said, pointing to Juan.

"Oh, she left some time ago," the young man said.

"Where to?" Juan asked tensely.

"Over to the other side of the mountain," the young man replied, pointing to the vague outline of mountains in the night sky.

"How did she get there?" Juan asked, trying to hide his impatience.

"By horse," the young man answered. "They came on horseback to get her because someone had broken his leg."

"Well, then, I need a horse, too," Juan said urgently.

"Tomorrow," the young man replied softly. "Perhaps I can take you tomorrow, maybe the next day. First I must finish harvesting the corn."

So Juan spent the next day in the fields, bathed in sweat from sunup to sundown.

Yet each ear of corn that he picked seemed to bring him closer to his treasure. And later that evening, when he helped the young man husk several ears so they could boil them for supper, the yellow kernels glittered like gold coins.

While they were eating, Juan thought about Doña Josefa. Why, he wondered, would someone who said she was the world's richest woman spend her time taking care of every sick person for miles around?

The following day, the two set off at dawn. Juan could not recall when he last had noticed the beauty of the sunrise. He felt strangely moved by the sight of the mountains, barely lit by the faint rays of the morning sun.

As they neared the foothills, the young man said, "I'm not surprised you're looking for Doña Josefa. The whole countryside needs her. I went for her because my wife had been running a high fever. In no time at all, Doña Josefa had her on the road to recovery. And what's more, my friend, she brought her a gold coin!"

Juan groaned inwardly. To think that someone could hand out gold so freely! What a strange woman Doña Josefa is, Juan thought. Not only is she willing to help one person after another, but she doesn't mind traveling all over the countryside to do it!

"Well, my friend," said the young man finally, "this is where I must leave you. But you don't have far to walk. See that house over there? It belongs to the man who broke his leg."

The young man stretched out his hand to say good-bye. Juan stared at it for a moment. It had been a long, long time since the thief had shaken hands with anyone. Slowly, he pulled out a hand from under his poncho. When his companion grasped it firmly in his own, Juan felt suddenly warmed, as if by the rays of the sun.

But after he thanked the young man, Juan ran down the road. He was still eager to catch up with Doña Josefa. When he reached the house, a woman and a child were stepping down from a wagon.

"Have you seen Doña Josefa?" Juan asked.

"We've just taken her to Don Teodosio's," the woman said. "His wife is sick, you know—"

"How do I get there?" Juan broke in. "I've got to see her."

"It's too far to walk," the woman said amiably. "If you'd like, I'll take you there tomorrow. But first I must gather my squash and beans."

So Juan spent yet another long day in the fields. Working beneath the summer sun, Juan noticed that his skin had begun to tan. And although he had to stoop down to pick the squash, he found that he could now stretch his body. His back had begun to straighten, too.

Later, when the little girl took him by the hand to show him a family of rabbits burrowed under a fallen tree, Juan's face broke into a smile. It had been a long, long time since Juan had smiled.

Yet his thoughts kept coming back to the gold.

The following day, the wagon carrying Juan and the woman lumbered along a road lined with coffee fields.

The woman said, "I don't know what we would have done without Doña Josefa. I sent my daughter to our neighbor's house, who then brought Doña Josefa on horseback. She set my husband's leg and then showed me how to brew a special tea to lessen the pain."

Getting no reply, she went on. "And, as if that weren't enough, she brought him a gold coin. Can you imagine such a thing?"

Juan could only sigh. No doubt about it, he thought, Doña Josefa is someone special. But Juan didn't know whether to be happy that Doña Josefa had so much gold she could freely hand it out, or angry for her having already given so much of it away.

When they finally reached Don Teodosio's house, Doña Josefa was already gone. But here, too, there was work that needed to be done. . . .

Juan stayed to help with the coffee harvest. As he picked the red berries, he gazed up from time to time at the trees that grew, row upon row, along the hillsides. What a calm, peaceful place this is! he thought.

The next morning, Juan was up at daybreak. Bathed in the soft, dawn light, the mountains seemed to smile at him. When Don Teodosio offered him a lift on horseback, Juan found it difficult to have to say good-bye.

"What a good woman Doña Josefa is!" Don Teodosio said, as they rode down the hill toward the sugarcane fields. "The minute she heard about my wife being sick, she came with her special herbs. And as if that weren't enough, she brought my wife a gold coin!"

In the stifling heat, the kind that often signals the approach of a storm, Juan simply sighed and mopped his brow. The pair continued riding for several hours in silence.

Juan then realized he was back in familiar territory, for they were now on the stretch of road he had traveled only a week ago—though how much longer it now seemed to him. He jumped off Don Teodosio's horse and broke into a run.

This time the gold would not escape him! But he had to move quickly, so he could find shelter before the storm broke.

Out of breath, Juan finally reached Doña Josefa's hut. She was standing by the door, shaking her head slowly as she surveyed the ransacked house.

"So I've caught up with you at last!" Juan shouted, startling the old woman. "Where's the gold?"

"The gold coin?" Doña Josefa said, surprised and looking at Juan intently. "Have you come for the gold coin? I've been trying hard to give it to someone who might need it," Doña Josefa said. "First to an old man who had just gotten over a bad attack. Then to a young woman who had been running a fever. Then to a man with a broken leg. And finally to Don Teodosio's wife. But none of them would take it. They all said, 'Keep it. There must be someone who needs it more.'"

Juan did not say a word.

"You must be the one who needs it," Doña Josefa said.

She took the coin out of her pocket and handed it to him. Juan stared at the coin, speechless.

At that moment a young girl appeared, her long braid bouncing as she ran. "Hurry, Doña Josefa, please!" she said breathlessly. "My mother is all alone, and the baby is due any minute."

"Of course, dear," Doña Josefa replied. But as she glanced up at the sky, she saw nothing but black clouds. The storm was nearly upon them. Doña Josefa sighed deeply.

"But how can I leave now? Look at my house! I don't know what has happened to the roof. The storm will wash the whole place away!"

And there was a deep sadness in her voice.

Juan took in the child's frightened eyes, Doña Josefa's sad, distressed face, and the ransacked hut.

"Go ahead, Doña Josefa," he said. "Don't worry about your house. I'll see that the roof is back in shape, good as new."

The woman nodded gratefully, drew her cloak about her shoulders, and took the child by the hand. As she turned to leave, Juan held out his hand.

"Here, take this," he said, giving her the gold coin. "I'm sure the newborn will need it more than I."

TRANSFORMATION

...through Dance

The Student

When he was seven, Jacques d'Amboise had to sit through his sister's ballet class. *What a pain!* he thought. But then, the teacher invited him to join in and make some big jumps. That invitation transformed his life. "Half of my friends grew up to become policemen and the other half gangsters—and I became a ballet dancer," he says.

The Teacher

D'Amboise joined the New York City Ballet when he was fifteen and has been involved in dance for more than forty years. Since 1976, d'Amboise has been teaching thousands of children to dance through his National Dance Institute (NDI). Many come from poor neighborhoods, much like the one in which d'Amboise grew up.

The Teacher's Student

Now meet John Karol, a 14-year-old NDI student, who talks about how dancing—and d'Amboise—have changed his life.

Question: How did you start dancing?

Answer: When I was in the fifth grade, I got a notice that Jacques d'Amboise was putting together a dance program. I had French class. I really hated French, so I decided to take dance.

Q: What was your first impression of the class?

A: From the first moment, I liked it. Jacques made it into a game or contest. Pretty soon, he'd have everyone on the stage—all jumping to music and in time, of course.

Q: What did your friends think about your taking dance classes?

A: At first, they made fun of me. Then, they saw a performance and realized what it was like, that it wasn't with tutus or little ballet slippers. They saw that we wore great costumes and had a great time on stage. After that, all the boys wanted to try out for Jacques's class.

Q: Is there anything special about how d'Amboise teaches?

A: Jacques tells us stories to get us interested. One he tells is about how he lived in a pretty bad neighborhood with gangs. When he was teased about dancing, Jacques asked, "Well, can you do this?" He took a running jump and leaped over a parked car. "Ballet taught me how to do that," he said.

Q: How has dancing changed you as a person?

A: Dancing has made me more outgoing so that I can speak for myself and voice my opinions. I've also made a lot more friends.

John Karol rehearses his role as one of the Three Musketeers for a performance.

The Shimmershine

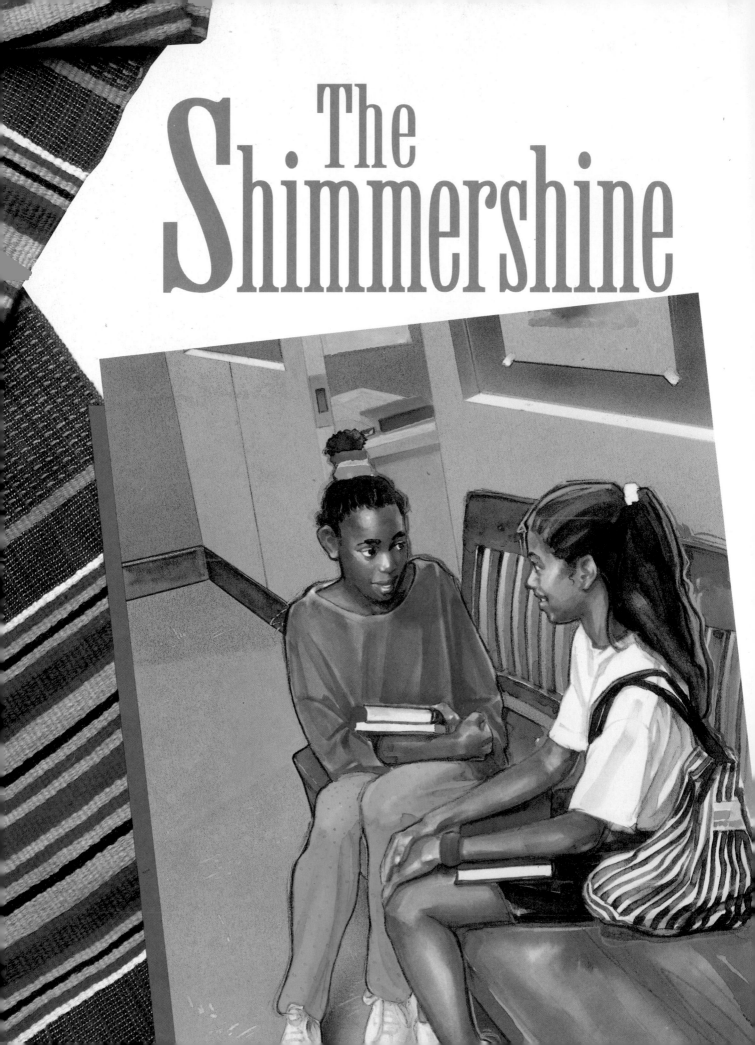

Queens

by Camille Yarbrough

illustrated by Cornelius Van Wright

When you are as shy as Angie and live in a tough city neighborhood, feeling good about yourself can be hard sometimes. You need to be strong, like Great Cousin Seatta, who told Angie about the "shimmer-shine feeling"—a feeling of pride in who you are and where you come from. Having a good teacher can help, too, and Angie believes that Ms. Collier, the new drama and dance instructor, will make a real difference. She and Michelle, her best friend, just hope that Ms. Collier stays longer than their last drama teacher.

Wednesday morning, before they went to class, Angie and Michelle walked into the principal's office and sat down on the bench just inside the door. After watching them a while, the secretary asked, "Are you two waiting for the principal?"

"Who?" Angie and Michelle looked at each other. "The principal? No, we waitin for Ms. Collier. Did she come in yet?"

"No," the secretary answered, "I haven't seen her yet."

"Did she quit?" Angie asked.

"I don't know. I don't think so." The secretary looked at them, frowning. "Can someone else help you?"

"No, we just wanna see Ms. Collier." Michelle smiled.

"Who wants to see me?"

Angie and Michelle felt caught. They hadn't intended for Ms. Collier to see them. If she hadn't quit, they thought she would come in through the door near the time clock on the other side of the room, but she came in the door next to where they were sitting, and there she stood, looking at them. They both stood up at the same time. "Good morning, Ms. Collier," they sang out.

"Good morning," she said, smiling. "You want to see me about something?"

"We just wanted to see if you was coming back." Michelle grinned as she and Angie circled Ms. Collier and waved as they hurried past her and out of the door she had come in.

"I told you she was comin back," Michelle bragged as they rushed up the stairs.

"Yeah. Did you see those big boxes she had?"

"Yeah, she got sumpum for us."

"I'm gon tell everybody she got sumpum for us. Everybody but Charlene." Angie laughed.

Later, in the lunchroom, the younger students

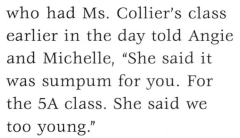

who had Ms. Collier's class earlier in the day told Angie and Michelle, "She said it was sumpum for you. For the 5A class. She said we too young."

"It's just for our class?" Angie and Michelle were thrilled.

When lunch was finished and they were back in class, Angie and Michelle spread

the word about Ms. Collier's surprise. "It's just for us," they bragged. And when Ms. Collier came to get them and told them to go on ahead in the hall, the line formed quickly and moved to the top of the stairway with Angie and Michelle leading the way. They stopped the line there and waited for Ms. Collier to come to the front. "Be cool," Michelle whispered. No one moved or broke the line or laughed or screamed. They waited and watched Ms. Collier and she watched them, holding her breath, delighted when one of them asked, "You got sumpum for us?" And especially when Charlene asked, "You like us, Ms. Collier?"

The line descended without a shout or a shove. As they approached Ms. Collier's room, Charlene lost faith. "We ain't gon do nothin special," she warned. "Just wait and see." This time her warning was answered by a chorus of sucked teeth, and rolled eyes and grins from Angie and Michelle. When the door was opened, the double line of children surged forward into the room. They stopped in the center. Their eyes wide, they turned in circles to see the surprise.

"Isn't it grand?" Angie sang the words, spacing them.

Lengths of red, brown, yellow, purple, and mixed-color fabrics stretched from the ceiling of the room, crossed in front of the windows, and dropped onto carved Ghanaian stools set in opposite corners. Calabash bowls, feathered fans, brass and iron bracelets, anklets, and earrings covered the table. Long cowrie-shell collars, beaded veils, and elephant tail whisks hung from the top of the blackboard; gold and silver lace, grand Buba gowns tacked in place, were spread out and glistening, hiding the wooden sliding-door cabinet. The

soft gourd and metal music of the African Kalimba flowed from the tape machine hidden beneath the table, and the scent of incense filled the room, changing it into an exciting place of new sounds, scents, colors, and shapes. Ms. Collier had overdressed and in the corner of the room quickly took off her long overgarment, and as the Kalimba music changed to drum rhythms, the children turned to see the golden fabric of a grand Buba gown billow around Ms. Collier as she whirled and stretched and bent, dancing toward them.

The class "Yayed" and clapped and formed a circle around her, some ululating in their delight. Angie couldn't believe what was happening. The classroom was now like her dreaming room when she got the golden shimmershine feeling. And just as she always danced in her dreaming room, Angie stepped into the dancing circle with Ms. Collier and danced. As she moved, the brilliant colors that draped the room, the young faces, the carved and woven shapes, all blurred around her. Only Ms. Collier was clear, and Angie mirrored her movements, turning, jumping, twisting when she did. The class was stunned and whooped their delight. Even Charlene and her gang were impressed. This was not the scaredy-cat Angie they knew. This was a new Angie and she could dance.

Michelle led the squeals of delight and the applause when the dance ended. Angie looked at Ms. Collier, thinking maybe she had done wrong to dance with her. Ms. Collier saw the question and the fear. "It's all right, Angie. We're happy that you danced. You were great. Wasn't she, class?"

With barely a smile, Angie watched her classmates applaud her, even Charlene, Cheryl, and Pat. Angie felt strange and she didn't understand the feeling. "You got the shimmershine," Michelle whispered in her ear.

"Yeah." Angie finally smiled. But it wasn't just the shimmershine. Something else was happening.

"All right, class." Ms. Collier waved her hands, directing them to bring their chairs into a semicircle around her. "I have something to ask you. Would you like"—Ms. Collier sat down on her tall stool—"to do a play?"

"Yes," the class answered. Angie and Michelle exchanged smiles but Angie was still in her shimmershine dream world.

"The play," Ms. Collier explained, "starts in Africa, then moves to America. The beautiful clothes, fabric, and jewelry you see all around come from Africa and are part of what you will wear in the play."

"Yeah!" the class responded.

"What's in the box?" Hector stood up and asked. "You got sumpum else for us?"

"Let us see what you got," others asked.

Ms. Collier opened the box that she had placed on her desk. From the box she lifted a pair of children's-size pants, a shirt, and a dress. They were drab and torn and made of coarse cloth.

"What's that?" Charlene scowled.

"They are not beautiful, are they? Not something you would like to wear."

"No," the class moaned, and frowned.

"They all raggedy," Darrell observed. "They got holes in um."

Angie stared at the sad clothing. Great Cousin Seatta's words came to her. "Some didn't have no shoes and day clothes was raggedy." "Ms. Collier"—Angie raised her hand—"I think I know what they are."

"Good. What do you think they are, Angie?"

Angie's voice was almost a whisper when she answered, "I think they slave children's clothes."

"Ooooh! Slave children's clothes," Cheryl moaned. "We got to be slaves in the play?" She sucked her teeth and slouched in her chair.

Hector stood up abruptly. "Not me! I'm not gon do the play if I have to be a slave."

"You don't understand," Angie explained to the class. "They was like us."

"Oooh, no, they wasn't

like us neither. They was Africans."

"Let me tell you the story of the play. Then you tell me if you want to do it. Is that agreeable?"

Angie's "Yes" was louder than the rest as she sat forward in her chair to hear the story. The class became quiet, watching, listening.

"The play is called *The Dancing Children of Ghana.* The story begins in the seventeen hundreds, in Agogo, an Asante village in Ghana, West Africa. God had blessed the village with many children and, like all children, they loved to learn things and to play games. Some of the boys worked the bellows to fan a breeze for the Egofoo, the goldsmith, when he cast his metal jewelry and collected wood for the food fires. The girls helped the older women pound yam, care for the babies, keep the village clean, and make pottery. Most of all, the children loved two things. The first was to dance. Especially a dance called the Adewa. Whenever they heard the drummers playing Adewa, they would run to where the drummers were, where the villagers were gathering, and watch the adults dance. The children imitated their movements. They especially loved the hand movements that meant different things. One movement meant 'Let us unite.' Others meant 'We are strong,' and 'We are the best.' 'We are warriors,' or 'Whatever you do, enemy, we will get our way.' The children imitated the proud style of the dancers, the way the men wrapped their beautiful Kente cloth around them and stamped their feet to show their power over their enemy. The girls squinched their eyes when they danced, the way the adults did, to show disrespect and insult. And they touched their fists one on top of the other to show 'I have the power.'

"The second thing they loved to do was to draw proverb pictures in the loose soil under the large tree in the center of the village. One child would draw a picture of the two alligators with one stomach. One of the other children would have to guess what it meant."

"What did it mean?" Angie asked.

"It means 'We share life. We must have unity,'" Ms. Collier answered. "Then someone drew the picture of the bird that looks backwards, the Sankofa."

"What that mean?" asked Charlene.

"It means 'You can always correct what went wrong. Return and fetch what is yours.' If you couldn't tell what the proverb pictures meant, you were out of the game.

"Now comes the serious part." Ms. Collier spaced out her words. "One day, during the festival season, when everyone was praying, dancing, singing, and telling and listening to their history, from the surrounding forest European slave traders very quietly sneaked into the village and then attacked the people. With clubs the traders knocked them out. With long firesticks they shot some of the men. Everyone was tied up, even the children. Then they were made to walk for miles and miles to the coast. There the children were separated from the people of their village and put onto a ship that brought them to America, to a plantation in Alabama.

"They met other African people there. Many were Asante. All the African people took care of them as much as they could, but their lives were miserable and sad. The children saw that so many were whipped. So many cried and died. They were heartbroken.

Natilee is Yaa, born on Thursday

Dawn is Afua, born on Friday

Michelle is Amma, born on Saturday.

And Nia is our stage manager."

"What's that?" Nia asked.

"I'll tell you. Now the boys.

Darrell is Kwasi, born on Sunday

Hector is Kojo, born on Monday.

And because we only have two boys in our class, I am borrowing five boys from the other school where I teach when I'm not here. They won't be able to come before the day of the performance, but they already know the dances because we were working at their school before we came to work with you. I am very pleased that you want to do the play. But, as I said, the Arts in Action program started late in this school, and we only have a short time to work on it before the performance."

"That's all right, Ms. Collier," Michelle assured her. "We won't mess up."

"We only have six rehearsals."

"What we gonna wear?" Charlene stood up to ask. "If I'm gonna dance and act, I have to look good." She put her hands on her hips and styled. Michelle looked at Angie with big eyes, but Angie didn't look back.

"Angie." Michelle touched her arm. "What's the matter?"

Angie didn't answer.

"You gonna look bad." Ms. Collier posed like Charlene.

"Do it, Ms. Collier!" Cheryl laughed and jumped up to pose alongside Charlene. Darrell and Hector whistled.

"I'm going to give you two things to take home. Those of you who have someone at home who can sew, raise your hands. I will give you some fabric and a drawing of the slave costume.

It is very simple. The second thing I will give each of you is your script. Read it over carefully. Bring it back to our next class. Treat it nicely." Ms. Collier had walked to the table as she talked. The students were gathered around her and "oohed" and "aahed" when she showed them their African wraps and head ties. The room was noisy with their delight and excitement.

"She just gets depressed sometimes."

Ms. Collier took Angie's hand and led her to the mirror. "You come when you can. Now, let us see how you look in this." She began to wrap an amber cloth around Angie and roll it over tight at the top. "You want me to call your mother? Sometimes, when people get depressed, they feel better when they talk to someone about what's on their mind."

Although she was standing in front of the mirror, Angie did not look at herself in it. "Yeah," she said quietly, "she need to talk to somebody."

"Look at yourself. We gon be stars." Michelle put her arm around Angie's shoulder and smiled into the mirror. "We gon look just like twins. Look."

Angie looked at their reflection in the mirror, then looked away. "We don't look like no twins. You not as dark as me. Is she, Ms. Collier?"

Ms. Collier positioned them shoulder to shoulder. "Let me see. Michelle is a real nice dark brown with a little yellow and Angie is a real pretty dark brown with a little red. Just beautiful."

Angie looked straight at Ms. Collier. "Why you want me to be the storyteller in the play?"

"Because I think it will be good for you to speak in front of an audience and because I think you will do it well." Ms. Collier looked straight back at Angie.

"I won't look funny?"

"No."

"We look good, girl," Michelle bragged again in front of the mirror. "We are too fresh."

"I look different." Angie looked at herself.

Ms. Collier put her hands on her hips and styled in front of the mirror. "Angie, I think you look like me, and I think I am too fine, so I don't know what you are talking about."

"Ooh, Ms. Collier, you sumpum else." Angie and Michelle looked at each other and laughed.

"You numbers better 'sumpum else' on home. Go! I'm tired."

"Yeah, we betta go. We can't look at ourselves no more, we too gorgeous. We the shimmershine queens."

"The what?"

Angie and Michelle began to giggle. They collapsed on the table, burying their heads in the fabric.

"Come on, before you go, you have to tell me about the—what? Shimmershine queens?"

"That's the name my Great Cousin Seatta gave it. You know, like when you do sumpum good and you feel warm and shiny all over your body. That's the shimmershine."

"So you two are the shimmershine queens?"

Angie and Michelle helped Ms. Collier hang the remaining fabric and clothing in the cabinet. "We gon write a rap poem about it." Angie grinned, picking up her book bag and putting her fabric and drawing in it.

"Can you help us?" Michelle mirrored Angie's grin as she backed toward the door, her book bag on her back.

"Don't you two think I have enough work?" Ms. Collier collapsed into her chair at the desk. "Good-bye."

"Just a little bit?" Michelle pleaded from the door, with Angie looking over her shoulder.

"A little bit. Good-bye."

Angie and Michelle ran out into the schoolyard, making the ululation sound, startling the children still playing in the yard. They strutted and skipped down the street toward Columbus Avenue.

"I like Ms. Collier, don't you?"

"Yes, I think she gon stay."

202

Meet Camille Yarbrough

" . . . a people's story is the anchor dat keeps um from driftin, it's the compass to show the way to go and it's a sail dat holds the power dat takes um forward." These words, spoken by Great Cousin Seatta at one point in *The Shimmershine Queens,* reflect the outlook of the book's author, Camille Yarbrough.

Yarbrough first began to learn about African-American history and culture through dance. She studied to be a dancer for many years and was a member of the Katherine Dunham dance company. She not only performed on Broadway but also toured around the world with the cast of *To Be Young, Gifted, and Black.*

When jobs in theater became hard to find, Yarbrough turned to teaching. In the schools in the Upper West Side of New York City, her students were largely African-American, Latino, and Caribbean children. Believing that knowledge of their cultural heritage would build self-confidence, Yarbrough set out to teach that heritage through music and dance—much like the teacher in *The Shimmershine Queens.* Yarbrough has also been successful in communicating this heritage through her writing; her first book, *Cornrows,* won a Coretta Scott King Award.

Change

The summer
still hangs
heavy and sweet
with sunlight
as it did last year.

The autumn
still comes
showering gold and crimson
as it did last year.

The winter
still stings
clean and cold and white
as it did last year.

The spring
still comes
like a whisper in the dark night.

It is only I
who have changed.

Charlotte Zolotow

CONTENTS

Against THE Odds

The only way to define the limits of the possible is by going beyond them into the impossible.

ARTHUR C. CLARKE

the MARBLE

by Gary Soto

CHAMP

illustrated by Ken Spengler

BREAKER'S BRIDGE

by Laurence Yep

illustrated by David Wisniewski

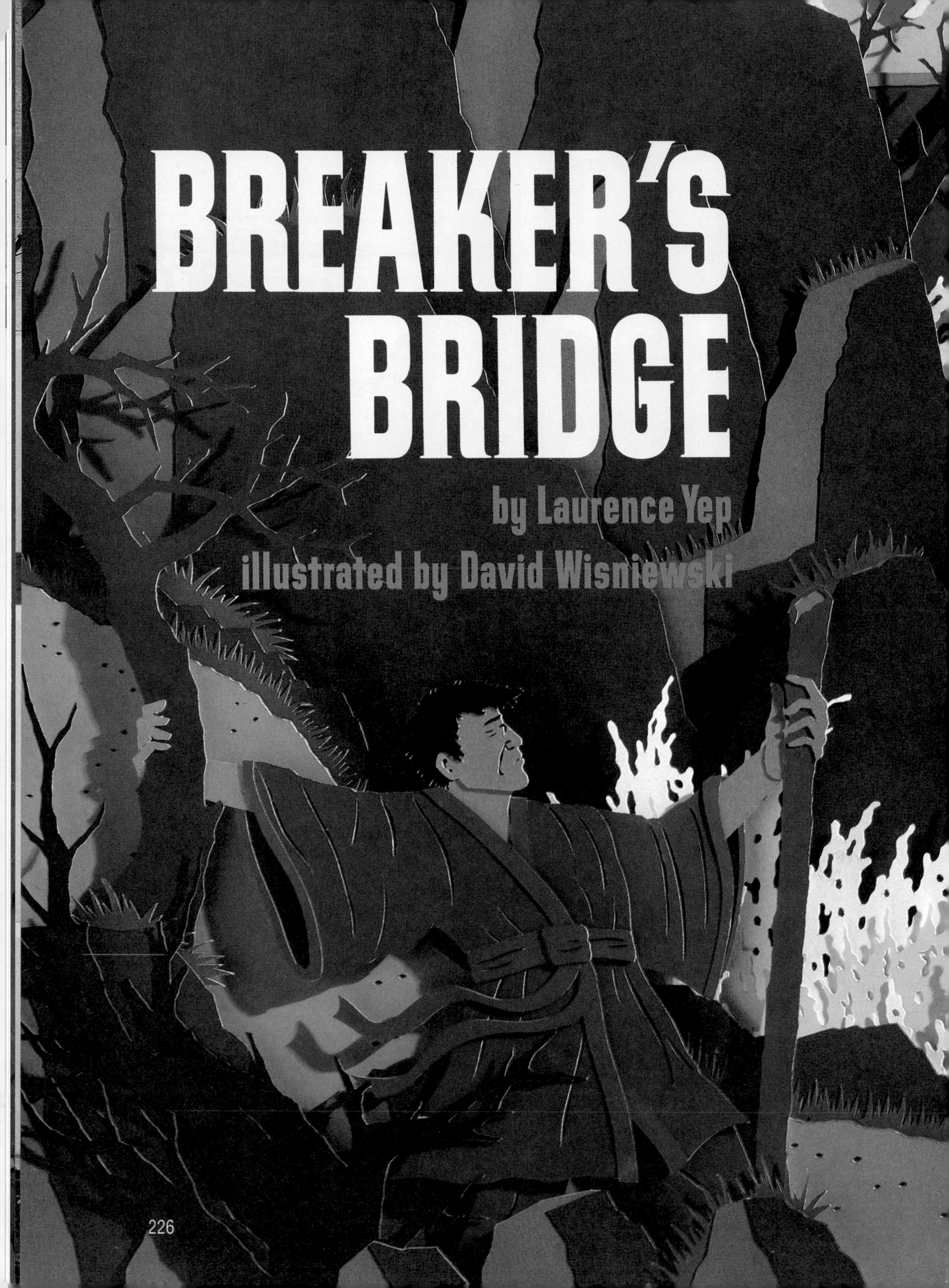

226

old man. Night's coming on and it gets cold up in these mountains."

"Can't." The old man nodded to his broken crutch.

Breaker looked all around. It was growing dark, and his stomach was aching with hunger. But he couldn't leave the old man stranded in the mountains, so Breaker took out his knife. "If I make you a new crutch, can you reach your home?"

"If you make me a crutch, we'll all have what we want." It was getting so dim that Breaker could not be sure if the old man smiled.

Although it was hard to see, Breaker found a tall, straight sapling and tried to trim the branches from its sides; but being Breaker, he dropped his knife several times and lost it twice among the old leaves on the forest floor. He also cut each of his fingers. By the time he was ready to cut down the sapling, he couldn't even see it. Of course, he cut his fingers even more. And just as he was trimming

L E A D

To Space and Back
by Sally Ride with Susan Okie
Beach Tree Books, 1991

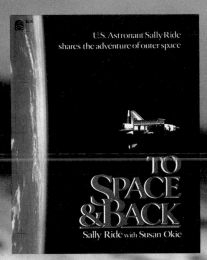

Black Star, Bright Dawn
by Scott O'Dell
Ballantine, 1990

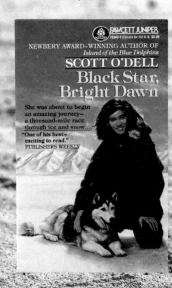

MEET
JILL KREMENTZ

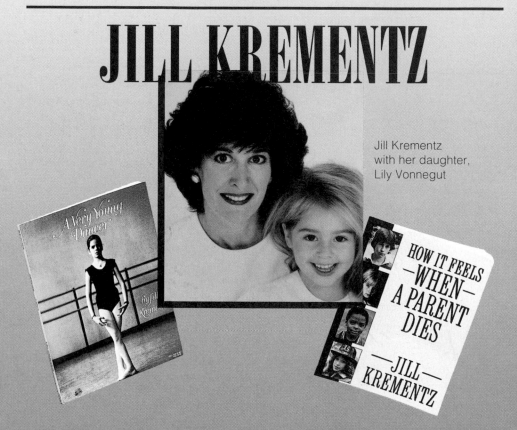

Jill Krementz with her daughter, Lily Vonnegut

Several years ago, Jill Krementz attended the funeral of a friend. There, she spotted her friend's son, a boy of about eight, bravely holding back tears. But when Krementz spoke to him, he let loose a flood of feelings. One of the strongest was his feeling of being alone. "That's when I decided to write *How It Feels When a Parent Dies*," Krementz said. "I wanted kids who have experienced the death of a parent to know that they are not alone."

Since then, Krementz has written three more *How It Feels* books. In each, Krementz tells the children's stories in a writer's voice that sounds like the children's own. For *How It Feels to Fight for Your Life,* she interviewed children who were very ill. Although such a book could be terribly sad, this one isn't. Krementz's interviews bring out the children's hopes, their courage—and their fears.

Krementz has photographed and written children's books on many other topics. The books in her *Very Young* series, including the award-winning *A Very Young Dancer,* look at children working hard to succeed in various fields.

HOW IT FEELS TO
FIGHT FOR YOUR LIFE

Rachel
DeMaster,
age ten

written and photographed
by Jill Krementz

"LAST YEAR
I LEARNED
TO GIVE
MYSELF
INJECTIONS."

I was seven years old when my mom told me I had diabetes. It was a big shock because other than having to go to the bathroom more than usual I was feeling fine. I had gone to my doctor for a regular checkup and he found sugar in my urine. This was a sign that my pancreas wasn't working right.

When my mother explained to me what diabetes was I burst into tears. I was afraid I was going to die. Even after my parents convinced me that this wasn't going to happen, I felt that my life was going to change completely.

My pancreas is in my tummy and it produces insulin. Insulin helps the body to process sugar and turn it into energy. There are two kinds of diabetes, Type One and Type Two. In Type One the pancreas can't produce insulin at all. In Type Two there's nothing wrong with the pancreas but the cells in the rest of the body don't respond to the insulin. Type One used to be called juvenile onset diabetes because it occurred most frequently among kids, but now they've learned that grown-ups can also get Type One. I have Type One, which means that I have to get insulin shots.

I was really lucky that my pediatrician noticed a problem so quickly because we were able to start treatment right away. I was diagnosed in December and a couple of months later, when it was time for me to start taking insulin, I went to the hospital and stayed there for three days. I was in Mount Sinai Hospital in New York City, which has one of the best diabetes programs anywhere. I wasn't sick

low I feel shaky and dizzy and blah. Sometimes it gives me a slight headache, too. All I can do is sit. I don't have lows every day but there are days when I have two or three. Usually it depends on how much exercise I'm getting and how the day is going. Sometimes it's hard to distinguish between having a low and feeling crummy. I might go down to the nurse's office and take my blood test and find I'm not low at all.

If I'm having a low and don't do anything for it for a couple of minutes, it won't do any damage. But if I don't get some sugar into my system quickly it can be dangerous. I've never fainted during a low but that's because I always treat it in time. I wear a Medic Alert necklace that tells people I'm an insulin-dependent diabetic. It has phone numbers on it for them to call in case of an emergency. That way, if I'm somewhere alone and I have a problem, people who don't know what's wrong with me will be able to get me help immediately.

My brother, Neil, is great about helping me with my lows. When I'm feeling shaky he'll get me some food so I don't have to get up and move around. He knows that if it's not too bad I should have milk and crackers and that I should drink orange juice if the low is more serious.

For me, the worst part of having diabetes is not being able to eat whatever I want. Unless I'm having a low I can't eat any sugar except the natural type that's in fruit. The sugar that's in candy and cake makes my blood sugar level very high for a long time after I eat it. Once in a while, on

"I GO TO THE SUPERMARKET WITH MY MOTHER AND HELP HER WITH THE SHOPPING."

"MY FAVORITE EXERCISE IS JOGGING WITH MY FATHER."

special occasions like my birthday, I have cake, but I'm basically not supposed to eat sweets. I feel bad when all my friends are eating candy and I can't have any. Neil is very considerate about not eating candy or cookies in front of me. He's older than I am and if he wants to eat sweets he usually waits until after I've gone to bed. There's one good thing about not eating sugar, which is that I don't have any cavities! My dentist is really proud of me.

On Halloween, my parents and I go trick or treating like everyone else, but since I can't eat the candy my parents buy it from me. They give me five cents for every piece of candy I get and I buy myself a stuffed animal. I have a great collection now. Neil used to eat all of my candy but since he got braces my parents have been buying his candy too.

I would have to say that I miss maple syrup the most of all the things I'm not allowed to eat. I go to the supermarket with my mother and help her with the shopping. We get stuff like diet soda and sugar-free hot chocolate so I don't miss sweet things too much. We spend a long time reading the labels on everything. It's amazing how many foods that don't taste sweet actually have sugar in them.

The worst thing about my diet is that I have to eat so much! Besides breakfast, lunch, and dinner, I have three snacks every day. People with diabetes have to eat a certain amount of carbohydrates and more protein than most people. This is a pain because I'm not a big eater and especially because I don't like protein. The morning snack we have at school is at just the right time for my first snack of the day. I always have milk and a carbohydrate. When I get home at three-thirty my mom

I have only one friend with diabetes. Her name is Tory and she's nine years old. Dr. Ginsberg introduced us at the hospital and we go to each other's house. If Tory hadn't taken a blood test with me, I never would have thought she had diabetes. She seems very healthy and she doesn't talk about it very much. I don't like to talk about diabetes either but I do like to know all about it. My family subscribes to a magazine called *Forecast,* which has all the latest news about machines and shots and what's going on medically. The best thing about *Forecast* is the section called "Making Friends." You can write to other people with diabetes. It has separate sections for people of all different ages and there's one section called "Friendly People 12 and Under." I think it would be fun to have a pen pal.

I also think it would be fun to go away to a special sleep-away camp for kids with diabetes. I can't go this year because my parents say I'm not old enough but I hope I can next year.

Sometimes I wonder if when I grow up anyone will want to marry me because my children may have diabetes. I worry that it's hereditary because my grandfather had it. My mother told me that it wouldn't be a problem because when people are really in love, the relationship comes first. My brother says that I shouldn't even be thinking about marriage for another fifteen years. He's right! Besides, by then there may be a cure for diabetes. In the meantime, things are okay because no matter what happens, I'm still me.

"...NO
MATTER WHAT
HAPPENS, I'M
STILL ME."

For POETs

by Al Young

Stay beautiful
but dont stay down underground
  too long
Dont turn into a mole
or a worm
or a root
or a stone

Come on out into the sunlight
Breathe in trees
Knock out mountains
Commune with snakes
& be the very hero of birds

Dont forget to poke your head up
& blink
think
Walk all around
Swim upstream

Dont forget to fly

259

years at the large nonreservation boarding school at Rapid City, South Dakota.

At Rapid City my father met my mother. They fell in love and were married and continued living and working there. My father was disappointed that he did not have a son but soon reconciled himself to his three daughters.

We were very lucky to have parents who taught us about our cultural background and who tried as the Lakotas had for generations to tell us the stories they had heard in their youth. After they were dead, I found several of the stories written out in my mother's and father's handwriting.

My father became very well known for his activities, first with The Society of American Indians. He was much sought after by many organizations as a speaker and soon became known as a "bridge between two cultures."

He spoke out many times critically, and in such a way that he was considered a spokesman for the Sioux.

My father presided at the ceremonies at Deadwood, South Dakota, when the Sioux inducted President Calvin Coolidge into the tribe.

Despite his distaste for the way in which the American Indian was depicted in movies he was persuaded to play a leading role in *The Silent Enemy,* written and produced by Douglas Burden, a trustee of the American Museum of Natural History. This was the first movie produced with an all-Indian cast and no professional actors. It was the story of the Ojibways' struggle against their silent enemy, hunger.

During this time he was also running for Congress in his home state of South Dakota.

He did the talking prologue for the picture *The Silent Enemy;* since the prologue was made in New York City studios, it was last to be filmed. During that time he caught a cold that became pneumonia. He died at the Rockefeller Institute Hospital after a brief illness.

Shortly after my father's death President Coolidge, usually a man of few words, wrote a wonderful tribute to him. In part he said, "He represented a trained and intelligent contact between two different races. He was a born leader who realized that the destiny of the Indian is indissolubly bound up with the destiny of our country. His loyalty to his tribe and his people made him a most patriotic American."

266

TONWEYA
AND THE
EAGLES

Everyone was excited. It was the Month of Grass Appearing, and the whole camp was busy getting ready to move over the plains to a new home. They would be close to more game and they looked forward to the move. Everyone that is except Chano. He loved this camping spot and already felt lonely for the distant hills.

Tahcawin had packed the parfleche cases with clothing and food and strapped them to a travois made of two trailing poles with a skin net stretched between them. Another travois lay on the ground ready for the new tipi.

Chano was very happy when Tasinagi suggested the three of them ride up to their favorite hills for the last time.

As the three of them rode along, Tasinagi called Chano's attention to the two large birds circling overhead. They were Waŋbli, the eagle. Chano knew they were sacred to his people and that they must never be killed.

He looked at the eagle feather in his father's hair, a sign of bravery, and wondered why it was that the Lakotas as well as many other Indians held Waŋbli, the eagle, in

"Tonweya carefully lowered himself over the edge of the cliff and soon stood on the ledge. There were two beautiful young eaglets in the nest, full feathered, though not yet able to fly. He tied them to his rope and prepared to climb up. But just as he placed his weight on the rope, to his great surprise it fell down beside him. The green hide had been slipping at the knot where he had tied it to the tree; when he pulled on it to go up again, the knot came loose and down came the rope.

"Tonweya realized immediately that he was trapped. Only Wakan-tanka, the Great Mystery, could save him from a slow death by starvation and thirst. He looked below him. There was a sheer drop of many hundreds of feet with not even the slightest projection by which he might climb down. When he tried to climb up, he could find neither handhold nor foothold. Wanbli had chosen well the place for a nest.

"Despite his brave heart terror gripped Tonweya. He stood looking off in the direction he knew his people to be. He cried out, '*Ma hiyopo! Ma hiyopo!* Help me!' but only the echo of his own voice answered.

his bow and arrows were just where he had left them. He managed to kill a rabbit upon which he and his eagle friends feasted. Late in the afternoon he reached the camp, only to find that his people had moved on. It was late. He was very tired so he decided to stay there that night. He soon fell asleep, the two eagles pressing close beside him all night.

"The sun was high in the sky when Tonweya awoke. The long sleep had given him back much strength. After once more giving thanks to Wakan-tanka for his safety he set out after his people. For two days he followed their trail. He lived on the roots and berries he found along the way and what little game he could shoot. He shared everything with his eagle brothers, who followed him. Sometimes they flew over-head, sometimes they walked behind him, and now and then they rested on his shoulders.

"Well along in the afternoon of the second day he caught up with the band. At first they were frightened when they saw him. Then they welcomed him with joy.

"They were astonished at his story. The two eagles who never left Tonweya amazed them. They were glad that they had always been kind to Waŋbli and had never killed them.

"The time came when the eagles were able to hunt food for themselves and though everyone expected them to fly away, they did not. True, they would leave with the dawn on hunting forays, but when the evening drew near, they would fly back fearlessly and enter Tonweya's tipi, where they passed the night. Everyone marveled at the sight.

"But eagles, like men, should be free. Tonweya, who by now understood their language, told them they could go. They were to enjoy the life the Great Mystery, Wakan-tanka, had planned for them. At first they refused. But when Tonweya said if he ever needed their help he would call for them, they consented.

"The tribe gave a great feast in their honor. In gratitude for all they had done Tonweya painted the tips of their wings a bright red to denote courage and bravery. He took them up on a high mountain. He held them once more toward the sky and bidding them good-bye released them. Spreading their wings they soared away. Tonweya watched them until they disappeared in the eye of the sun.

"Many snows have passed and Tonweya has long been dead. But now and then the eagles with the red-tipped wings are still seen. There are always two of them and they never show any fear of people. Some say they are the original sacred eagles of Tonweya, for the Waŋbli lives for many snows. Some think they are the children of the sacred ones. It is said whoever sees the red-tipped wings of the eagles is sure of their protection as long as he is fearless and brave. And only the fearless and brave may wear the eagle feather tipped with red."

When Tasinagi finished the story, he looked to see if the red-winged eagles were still following them. They were there. He knew then that his son Chano was one of those to be blessed by great good in his life.

I knew turning my ankle was a bad omen. Mama always says bad things happen in threes, so I knew I probably had two more coming. Or maybe, I thought, coming to East Oakland was the first bad thing and I was already on my second one.

Sometimes when two bad things happen, Mama will purposely break something she doesn't care about and say, "There! That's the third bad thing. Now we're finished."

I wished I could get my two more bad things over with fast, but I certainly couldn't break any of Auntie Hata's dishes. She didn't have that many to spare.

What really made me feel so awful about the whole thing was that Auntie Hata didn't get mad when I told her what I'd done. What she said was, "Ah, well, Rinko, I guess you're still only a child after all."

And she put cold compresses on my ankle and kept me off my feet, which made me feel worse than if she'd gotten mad and scolded me for being so stupid. Mama might just as well have sent Joji, I thought, for all the help I was to Auntie Hata.

As soon as my ankle was better, I tried to make up for everything and be a more responsible person. I was still limping, but I could help Auntie Hata hang out her wash, which she scrubbed in a big metal tub heated on the wood stove. And I ironed her sheets and pillow-cases so she'd have nice smooth sheets to sleep on. I could see why she usually didn't bother and why her clothes looked wrinkled. Ironing wasn't easy when you had to heat a big heavy iron on the wood stove.

I also swept out the whole house, which wasn't hard since there were no rugs, and I used damp tea leaves to keep down the dust. It didn't matter what day I cleaned, because Auntie Hata didn't have a special day for it like Mama, who wants it done on Saturdays.

Auntie Hata stopped eating and looked at me thoughtfully. Then she said, "He's had some hard times." As though that would explain everything.

"Like what?"

I could tell Auntie Hata was thinking carefully what to say, like Papa when he rubs his mustache.

"It's not always easy to make a life for yourself in a strange land," she said. "Sometimes . . . often, you're afraid, and you close yourself off and shut people out."

I could understand that. I've felt that way myself lots of times even if I'm *not* in a strange land. But I wondered why the old man should be afraid of me or my friends?

"Aw, the old man ain't afraid of nothing," Zenny said.

"He sure ain't," Abu agreed.

But Auntie Hata didn't seem to hear them. "We all get scared sometimes," she said. "And lonely too. Oh, yes. Lonely lots of times."

"Well, you don't have to be lonely while I'm here," I reminded her.

Auntie Hata smiled, crinkling her eyes into two small crescent moons. "That's right, Rinko."

She reached over to pat my shoulder and then got up to clear the table, and I still didn't know a thing about the old man.

The second bad thing happened when I'd almost forgotten about the first one. It was a lot worse than my sprained ankle, and it didn't happen to me.

It happened just as we were going to take more cucumbers to the factory. We had loaded up the truck and were ready to leave when an old beat-up truck came rattling along, and I heard a sound like the honking of a tired goose.

I knew what it was when I saw the canvas flapping over the sides of the truck and a scale dangling in the back. It looked just like the truck of a Japanese peddler who comes to our house once a week on Thursday afternoons.

attention to us. I felt as though an egg beater was churning up my stomach and everything else all together. And I guess Auntie Hata felt the same way, because she kept twisting a handkerchief in her hands until it was almost in shreds. Every once in a while she would send Zenny to go ask somebody about Abu.

"What's happening to my brother?" he'd ask anybody in a white uniform.

And whoever he talked to would just say something like, "Everything's OK, sonny. Don't worry. Go sit down till your doctor comes to talk to you."

So we sat and waited and waited and waited, and by then I felt all ground up like the sesame seeds in Mama's mortar. When I went to look at a clock, it was almost six o'clock.

Finally a doctor came out and called, "Mrs. Hata?"

Auntie Hata shot up from the bench as if she'd exploded from a cannon. She had a hard time finding the right words to ask the doctor what she wanted to know. "My boy, he's OK? He's OK? Please?"

"Your boy has lost a lot of blood but we gave him a transfusion," the doctor said slowly. "There's been some nerve damage, and he may not regain full use of his right arm. But he's holding his own. You can go see him now in Ward C."

Auntie Hata was trying hard to understand, but she wasn't sure. "Abu's OK?" she asked me over and over. "He's OK?"

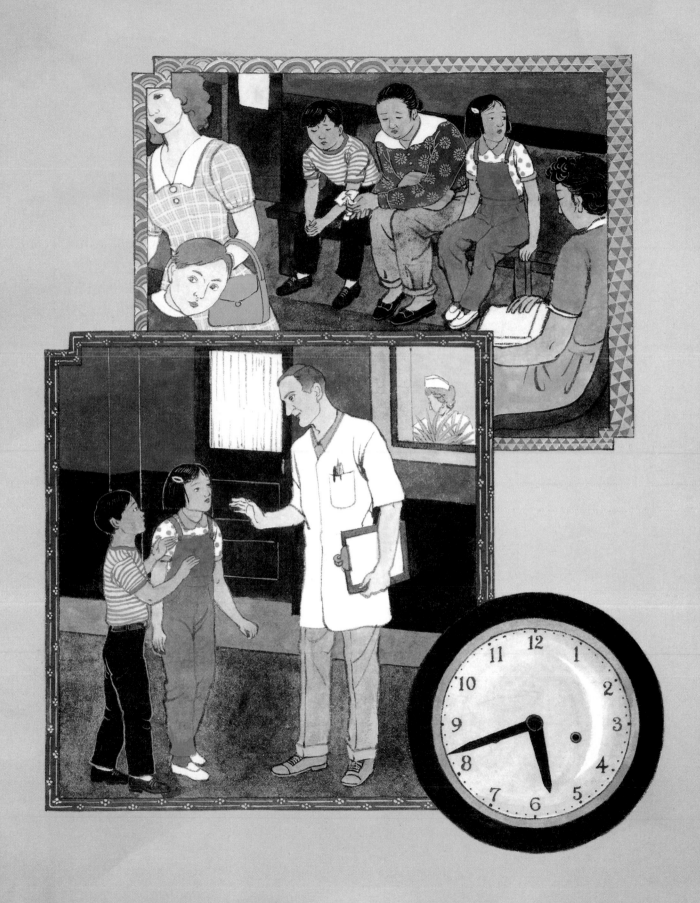

surprised to see us, he just froze with the egg turner clutched in his hand.

"Zenny! Rinko! What are you doing here?"

That was when Zenny and I both started talking, and I felt as though I was drowning in all the words that came tumbling out of my mouth. Between the two of us, we told the old man everything that had happened.

"And Abu? How is he now?" the old man asked when we finally stopped.

"The doctor said he had nerve damage," I said. "He's lost a lot of blood. Maybe . . . maybe he's going to die." I began to cry again.

For a minute the old man didn't know what to do with us. Then he went to talk to a bald-headed white man in a rumpled gray sweater who was sitting at the cash register. He called him Mr. Sabatini, and I guess he was the owner of the cafe. When the old man came back, he told us to sit down at the counter and he'd make us something to eat.

"I get off soon," he said, "and by the time you finish eating, I'll be ready to go home with you."

Then the old man was making toast, breaking eggs on the grill, and frying two ham steaks and some potatoes. It was like the time I'd seen him painting the samurai on his kite. His hands were steady and sure and knew exactly what to do without the old man's even having to think about it. I never saw anybody cook so fast. And suddenly everything was there in front of me, hot and sizzling, on a thick white plate, and it smelled so wonderful I nearly fainted.

Zenny and I pitched in and ate as though we hadn't seen any food for three weeks. It was strange eating breakfast for supper, but I'd been eating lunch for breakfast every day at Auntie Hata's, and it didn't seem to make any difference to my stomach. I sopped up all the runny egg yolk with my toast and ate every bit of the ham and potatoes.

The old man kept an eye on us while he served some other customers, and for dessert he gave each of us a piece of apple pie. He also poured a little coffee into our milk, and I had two glasses.

"The truck. Our truck's gone!"

"The truck? The truck's gone?" I asked like an echo.

The old man made Auntie Hata sit down and told her to calm herself. "Are you sure you just didn't forget where you parked it?"

"No, no. I left it right by the entrance."

"That's right," I said remembering. We'd pulled up at the emergency entrance and piled out without giving the truck another thought.

"And you left the keys in it?" Zenny asked.

Auntie Hata nodded sadly. "The keys, the cucumbers, the truck . . . somebody's taken them all."

"Maybe somebody parked it for you," I said hopefully.

"I walked around that hospital three times looking for it," Auntie Hata said, shaking her head. "It's gone. Somebody's stolen our truck!"

There it was, I thought, feeling terrible. That was the third bad thing to happen. My ankle, Abu's accident, and now the truck. Things seemed to be going from bad to worse ever since I arrived, and I began to feel like a jinx on Auntie Hata's life.

"I'll call Papa. He'll think of something." I started to get up and then remembered there was no phone in the house and that I'd have to wait until the next day to call from the hospital.

"I'll speak to the cop who comes to The Eagle for coffee every morning," the old man said. "Maybe he can help you find your truck."

But nothing we said could cheer her up. "I can't earn a living without the truck," Auntie Hata said miserably.

She let out a low moan, as though all the energy was drifting out of her body, like air going out of a balloon.

"We're finished, old man," she said slowly. "I think we're finished."

As soon as I called Mama and Papa the next day, they rushed over to the hospital. And they brought Reverend Mitaka with them. He is a bachelor, who Tami's mother is dying to find a wife for, and he is so shy, he never looks up from his notes when he preaches. He also has bad eyes and wears such thick glasses he looks a little like an owl.

I wished Mama hadn't brought him, but I guess she thought he could comfort Auntie Hata. Or maybe she thought Abu would get better if he prayed over him. I was sincerely hoping he wouldn't, but Reverend Mitaka prayed all right. He put his hand on Abu's forehead, and we stood around his bed as if we were having a prayer meeting.

I was so embarrassed because everybody in the ward was staring at us. I kept my eyes open all the time, watching to see if Abu would open his, but he didn't. Zenny had his eyes open too and was making circles on the floor with his left toe.

When I was feeling like I wanted to sink right into the floor, Reverend Mitaka finally stopped, and Auntie Hata took him and Mama and Papa aside to tell them about Abu's arm.

gardening the way Mr. Hata used to. No, I don't need another truck. All I want is for Abu to get well."

"He will, Mrs. Hata," Mama said. "He will."

When it was time to leave, Mama took me aside. "Well, Rinko," she said. "Your two weeks are about up. Do you want to come home with us or will you stay until the end of the month?"

I was surprised she should even ask, but I guess she did it to make me realize what I'd already decided. I hadn't even thought about going home early.

"I can't leave," I said to Mama. "Auntie Hata *really* needs me now."

Mama put her arm around me and gave me a hard squeeze. "Good," she said. "I hoped you'd say that."

Papa checked with me too. "You're sure you're all right?" he asked. "You're sure you want to stay?"

"Sure, Papa," I said. "I've got some unfinished business in East Oakland."

Papa looked puzzled, but I couldn't tell him I had to stay to find out what was bothering the old man. And I didn't admit the real reason I wanted to stay, which was that I'd grown to like Auntie Hata. In fact, I liked her a lot.

MEET

YOSHIKO UCHIDA

Yoshiko Uchida wrote her first stories when she was only ten years old, using brown wrapping paper that she made into booklets. She also kept a journal. Because she grew up during the Great Depression of the 1930s, she learned to save things, like her books and journals. It's lucky that she did, because the memories she recorded helped her create the award-winning books she has written as an adult.

All of Uchida's books are about Japanese or Japanese-American characters. *The Best Bad Thing* is the second book in her trilogy about Rinko, a girl growing up in the hard times of the 1930s. Although these books don't describe Uchida's own life exactly, she says that a lot of herself is in Rinko.

Some of Uchida's memories of growing up are more pleasant than others. She spent the first twenty years of her life in pleasant neighborhoods in northern California. But in 1941, the Japanese attacked Pearl Harbor, and her life changed dramatically. Panicked about the possibility of more attacks and spies, the American government rounded up Japanese Americans who lived on the West Coast. Uchida wrote about her family's experiences in *Journey to Topaz* and later in the award-winning *Journey Home,* which continues the family's story after World War II.

Today, when Uchida talks to students about the camps, she always asks why they think she wrote about these experiences. "'You wrote about them so it won't happen again,' they say." But she also feels that her books have a larger message. "I hope my readers can be caring human beings who don't think in terms of labels—foreigners or Asians or whatever—but think of people as human beings. If that comes across, then I've accomplished my purpose."

my friend

my friend is
like bark
rounding a tree

he warms
like sun
on a winter day

he cools
like water
in the hot noon

his voice
is ready
as a spring bird

he is
my friend
and I
am his

Emily Hearn

317

Dear Mr.

Henshaw

by Beverly Cleary
illustrated by R. J. Shay

Leigh Botts wants to be a famous author someday. He's been corresponding with his favorite author, Boyd Henshaw, who suggests that he keep a diary. Through his diary, Leigh learns a lot about himself and about the many changes going on in his life. Leigh's in a new school in a new town. He isn't finding it easy to make friends, and on top of that, someone keeps stealing things from his lunchbag. One day he rigs up a burglar alarm for a lunchbox, and it really works!

Leigh's parents are divorced, and he really misses his father, who drives a truck cross-country and is on the road most of the time. When he calls his father unexpectedly one day, he is about to take another boy and his mother out for pizza. Leigh worries that his father might remarry.

He also has other things on his mind. There's a Young Writers' contest at his school, and the prize will be lunch with a "Famous Author." Leigh is hoping to win.

Tuesday, March 20

Yesterday Miss Neely, the librarian, asked if I had written anything for the Young Writers' Yearbook, because all writing had to be turned in by tomorrow. When I told her I hadn't, she said I still had twenty-four hours and why didn't I get busy? So I did, because I really would like to meet a Famous Author. My story about the ten-foot wax man went into the wastebasket. Next I tried to start a story called *The Great Lunchbox Mystery*, but I couldn't seem to turn my lunchbox experience into a story because I don't know who the thief (thieves) was (were), and I don't want to know.

Finally I dashed off a description of the time I rode
with my father when he was trucking the load of grapes
down Highway 152 through Pacheco Pass to a winery.
I put in things like the signs that said STEEP GRADE, TRUCKS
USE LOW GEAR and how Dad down-shifted and how skillful
he was handling a long, heavy load on the curves. I put
in about the hawks on the telephone wires and about that
high peak where Black Bart's lookout used to watch for
travelers coming through the pass so he could signal to
Black Bart to rob them, and how the leaves on the trees
along the stream at the bottom of the pass were turning
yellow and how good tons of grapes smelled in the sun.
I left out the part about the waitresses and the video
games. Then I copied the whole thing over in case neat-
ness counts and gave it to Miss Neely.

Saturday, March 24

Mom said I had to invite Barry over to our house for
supper because I have been going to his house after
school so often. We had been working on a burglar alarm
for his room which we finally got to work with some help
from a library book.

I wasn't sure Barry would like to come to our house
which is so small compared to his, but he accepted when
I invited him.

Mom cooked a casserole full of good things like ground
beef, chilies, tortillas, tomatoes and cheese. Barry said he
really liked eating at our house because he got tired of eating with a bunch of little sisters waving spoons and drum-
sticks. That made me happy. It helps to have a friend.

Barry says his burglar alarm still works. The trouble is,
his little sisters think it's fun to open his door to set it off.
Then they giggle and hide. This was driving his mother
crazy, so he finally had to disconnect it. We all laughed
about this. Barry and I felt good about making something
that worked even if he can't use it.

321

from My Scrapbook

Barry saw the sign on my door that said KEEP OUT MOM THAT MEANS YOU. He asked if my Mom really stays out of my room. I said, "Sure, if I keep things picked up." Mom is not a snoop.

Barry said he wished he could have a room nobody ever went into. I was glad Barry didn't ask to use the bathroom. Maybe I'll start scrubbing off the mildew after all.

Sunday, March 25

I keep thinking about Dad and how lonely he sounded and wondering what happened to the pizza boy. I don't like to think about Dad being lonesome, but I don't like to think about the pizza boy cheering him up either.

Tonight at supper (beans and franks) I got up my courage to ask Mom if she thought Dad would get married again. She thought awhile and then said, "I don't see how he could afford to. He has big payments to make on the truck, and the price of diesel oil goes up all the time, and when people can't afford to build houses or buy cars, he won't be hauling lumber or cars."

I thought this over. I know that a license for a truck like his costs over a thousand dollars a year. "But he always sends my support payments," I said, "even if he is late sometimes."

"Yes, he does that," agreed my mother. "Your father isn't a bad man by any means."

Suddenly I was mad and disgusted with the whole thing. "Then why don't you two get married again?" I guess I wasn't very nice about the way I said it.

Mom looked me straight in the eye. "Because your father will never grow up," she said. I knew that was all she would ever say about it.

Tomorrow they give out the Young Writers' Yearbook! Maybe I will be lucky and get to go have lunch with the Famous Author.

Today wasn't the greatest day of my life. When our class went to the library, I saw a stack of Yearbooks and could hardly wait for Miss Neely to hand them out. When I finally got mine and opened it to the first page, there was a monster story, and I saw I hadn't won first prize. I kept turning. I didn't win second prize which went to a poem, and I didn't win third or fourth prize, either. Then I turned another page and saw Honorable Mention and under it:

A DAY ON DAD'S RIG
by
Leigh M. Botts

There was my title with my name under it in print, even if it was mimeographed print. I can't say I wasn't disappointed because I hadn't won a prize, I was. I was really disappointed about not getting to meet the mysterious Famous Author, but I liked seeing my name in print.

Some kids were mad because they didn't win or even get something printed. They said they wouldn't ever try to write again which I think is pretty dumb. I have heard that real authors sometimes have their books turned down. I figure you win some, you lose some.

Then Miss Neely announced that the Famous Author the winners would get to have lunch with was Angela Badger. The girls were more excited than the boys because Angela Badger writes mostly about girls with problems like big feet or pimples or something. I would still like to meet her because she is, as they say, a real live author, and I've never met a real live author. I am glad Mr. Henshaw isn't the author because then I would *really* be disappointed that I didn't get to meet him.

Friday, March 30

Today turned out to be exciting. In the middle of second period Miss Neely called me out of class and asked if I would like to go have lunch with Angela Badger. I said, "Sure, how come?"

Miss Neely explained that the teachers discovered that the winning poem had been copied out of a book and wasn't original so the girl who submitted it would not be allowed to go and would I like to go in her place? Would I!

Miss Neely telephoned Mom at work for permission and I gave my lunch to Barry because my lunches are better than his. The other winners were all dressed up, but I didn't care. I have noticed that authors like Mr. Henshaw usually wear old plaid shirts in the pictures on the back of their books. My shirt is just as old as his, so I knew it was OK.

Miss Neely drove us in her own car to the Holiday Inn, where some other librarians and their winners were waiting in the lobby. Then Angela Badger arrived with Mr. Badger, and we were all led into the dining room which was pretty crowded. One of the librarians who was a sort of Super Librarian told the winners to sit at a long table with a sign that said Reserved. Angela Badger sat in the middle and some of the girls pushed to sit beside her. I sat across from her. Super Librarian explained that we could choose our lunch from the salad bar. Then all the librarians went off and sat at a table with Mr. Badger.

There I was face to face with a real live author who seemed like a nice lady, plump with wild hair, and I couldn't think of a thing to say because I hadn't read her books. Some girls told her how much they loved her books, but some of the boys and girls were too shy to say anything. Nothing seemed to happen until Mrs. Badger said, "Why don't we all go help ourselves to lunch at the salad bar?"

What a mess! Some people didn't understand about salad bars, but Mrs. Badger led the way and we helped ourselves to lettuce and bean salad and potato salad and all the usual stuff they lay out on salad bars. A few of the younger kids were too short to reach anything but the bowls on the first rows. They weren't doing too well until Mrs. Badger helped them out. Getting lunch took a long time, longer than in a school cafeteria, and when we carried our plates back to our table, people at other tables ducked and dodged as if they expected us to dump our lunches on their heads. All one boy had on his plate was a piece of lettuce and a slice of tomato because he thought he was going to get to go back for roast beef and fried chicken. We had to straighten him out and explain that all we got was salad. He turned red and went back for more salad.

"A Day On Dad's Rig"

by

Leigh M. Botts

I was still trying to think of something interesting to say to Mrs. Badger while I chased garbanzo beans around my plate with a fork. A couple of girls did all the talking, telling Mrs. Badger how they wanted to write books exactly like hers. The other librarians were busy talking and laughing with Mr. Badger who seemed to be a lot of fun.

Mrs. Badger tried to get some of the shy people to say something without much luck, and I still couldn't think of anything to say to a lady who wrote books about girls with big feet or pimples. Finally Mrs. Badger looked straight at me and asked, "What did you write for the Yearbook?"

I felt myself turn red and answered, "Just something about a ride on a truck."

"Oh!" said Mrs. Badger. "So you're the author of *A Day on Dad's Rig!*"

Everyone was quiet. None of us had known the real live author would have read what we had written, but she had and she remembered my title.

t A Mess!

HONORABLE MENTION

Young writer's yearbook

This is to certify that

Leigh M. Botts

completed with honors a written story about a personal experience
and is to be congratulated for an assignment well done.

Teacher   Author

"I just got honorable mention," I said, but I was thinking, *She called me an author. A real live author called me an author.*

"What difference does that make?" asked Mrs. Badger. "Judges never agree. I happened to like *A Day on Dad's Rig* because it was written by a boy who wrote honestly about something he knew and had strong feelings about. You made me feel what it was like to ride down a steep grade with tons of grapes behind me."

"But I couldn't make it into a story," I said, feeling a whole lot braver.

"Who cares?" said Mrs. Badger with a wave of her hand. She's the kind of person who wears rings on her forefingers. "What do you expect? The ability to write stories comes later, when you have lived longer and have more understanding. *A Day on Dad's Rig* was splendid work for a boy your age. You wrote like *you,* and you did not try to imitate someone else. This is one mark of a good writer. Keep it up."

I noticed a couple of girls who had been saying they wanted to write books exactly like Angela Badger exchange embarrassed looks.

"Gee, thanks," was all I could say. The waitress began to plunk down dishes of ice cream. Everyone got over being shy and began to ask Mrs. Badger if she wrote in pencil or on the typewriter and did she ever have books rejected and were her characters real people and did she ever have pimples when she was a girl like the girl in her book and what did it feel like to be a famous author?

I didn't think answers to those questions were very important, but I did have one question I wanted to ask which I finally managed to get in at the last minute when Mrs. Badger was autographing some books people had brought.

"Mrs. Badger," I said, "did you ever meet Boyd Henshaw?"

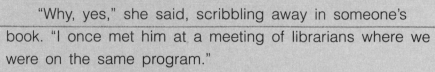

"Why, yes," she said, scribbling away in someone's book. "I once met him at a meeting of librarians where we were on the same program."

"What's he like?" I asked over the head of a girl crowding up with her book.

"He's a very nice young man with a wicked twinkle in his eye," she answered. I think I have known that since the time he answered my questions when Miss Martinez made us write to an author.

On the ride home everybody was chattering about Mrs. Badger this, and Mrs. Badger that. I didn't want to talk. I just wanted to think. A real live author had called *me* an author. A real live author had told me to keep it up. Mom was proud of me when I told her.

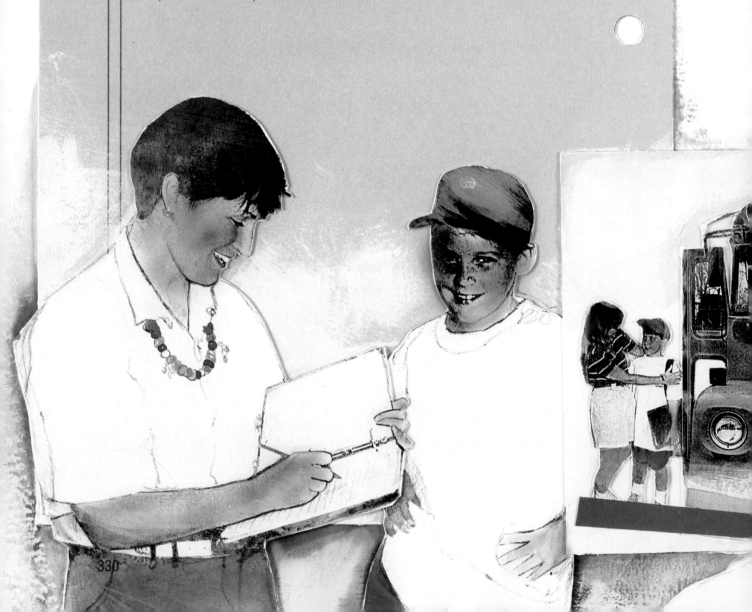

Meet Beverly Cleary

In 1982, Beverly Cleary received several letters from boys who had read her books. "Please," they suggested, "write a book about a boy whose parents are divorced." As she thought about this, she began to get ideas. She overheard a remark about a father who forgot to call his son as promised. She learned about a student who had rigged up a burglar alarm for his lunchbox. These bits and pieces went into the book. Cleary says, *"Dear Mr. Henshaw* was a most satisfying book to write. It seemed almost to write itself."

Surprisingly, Cleary was a poor reader when she began school. By the third grade, however, she had learned to read and to love books. In fact, her school librarian suggested that Cleary write children's books when she grew up. Cleary liked the idea but didn't write her first book until many years later. When she and her husband moved into a new house, they found several packages of blank paper in a closet. Her husband gave her a pencil sharpener, and she began to write. Her first book, *Henry Huggins,* was an instant success, as was its sequel, *Henry and Beezus.* Cleary has won many awards for her writing, including two Newbery Honor Awards for her books about a girl named Ramona and a Newbery Medal for *Dear Mr. Henshaw.*

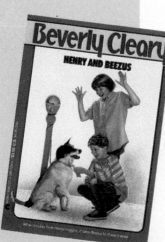

Who

am I?

The trees ask me,
And the sky,
And the sea asks me
    Who am I?

The grass asks me,
And the sand,
And the rocks ask me
    Who I am.

The wind tells me
At nightfall,
And the rain tells me
    Someone small.

    Someone small
    Someone small
    But a piece
        of
        it
        all.

by Felice Holman

Seekers Among US

Nelson Mandela and the Quest for Freedom

by Brian Feinberg ◆ Chelsea House, 1992

I need a neighbor who will live a teardrop away,
Who will open up when I knock late at night.
I need a child who will play a smile away.

(excerpt of a poem by Zindzi Mandela)

The Happiest Ending

by Yoshiko Uchida ◆ Atheneum, 1985

"Hey, Boku!" I hollered.
But all I heard was water dripping in
the basin in the upstairs hall.
"Mrs. Sugino, he's gone!" I yelled,
rushing back into the kitchen. "Boku's
disappeared!"

Ben and Me

An Astonishing Life of Benjamin Franklin
As written by his Good Mouse AMOS
Discovered, Edited & Illustrated by

ROBERT LAWSON

FOREWORD

The manuscript which forms this book was sent me recently by an architect friend. While altering an old Philadelphia house, workmen uncovered a small chamber beneath a bedroom hearthstone. This tiny room, for such it appeared to be, was about eighteen inches square. It contained various small articles of furniture, all of the Colonial Period. In one of these, a secretary desk, was found a manuscript book, the leaves of which, about the size of postage stamps, were covered with minute writing.

With the aid of a powerful reading-glass my friend managed to decipher the story which follows.

Scarce able to believe that such a remarkable document could be other than some ancient hoax, he sent it to various authorities for their opinions.

Scientists of the Brownsonian Institute have assured him that their analyses of the paper and ink prove them definitely to be of Early American manufacture, and that the writing was most certainly done with a quill pen of that period.

More startling still was the report from officials of the National Museum of Natural History, stating that, incredible as it might seem, there could be no possible doubt that the handwriting was that of—a mouse!

So without attempting any explanation, with only a few minor corrections of spelling and grammar, and the addition of some drawings, I give you Amos' story in his own words.

I am aware that his account of Franklin's career differs in many respects from the accounts of later historians. This I cannot explain but it seems reasonable to believe that statements made by one who lived on terms of such intimacy with this great man should be more trustworthy than those written by later scholars.

ROBERT LAWSON
Rabbit Hill
May, 1939

I, AMOS

Since the recent death of my lamented friend and patron Ben Franklin, many so-called historians have attempted to write accounts of his life and his achievements. Most of these are wrong in so many respects that I feel the time has now come for me to take pen in paw and set things right.

All of these ill-informed scribblers seem astonished at Ben's great fund of information, at his brilliant decisions, at his seeming knowledge of all that went on about him.

Had they asked me, I could have told them. It was ME.

For many years I was his closest friend and adviser and, if I do say it, was in great part responsible for his success and fame.

Not that I wish to claim too much: I simply hope to see justice done, credit given where credit is due, and that's to me—mostly.

Ben was undoubtedly a splendid fellow, a great man, a patriot and all that; but he *was* undeniably stupid at times, and had it not been for me—well, here's the true story, and you can judge for yourself.

I was the oldest of twenty-six children. My parents, in naming us, went right through the alphabet. I, being first, was **A**mos, the others went along through **B**athsheba, **C**laude, **D**aniel—and so forth down to the babies: **X**enophon, **Y**sobel, and **Z**enas.

We lived in the vestry of Old Christ Church on Second Street, in Philadelphia—behind the paneling. With that number of mouths to feed we were, naturally, not a very prosperous family. In fact we were really quite poor—as poor as church-mice.

But it was not until the Hard Winter of 1745 that things really became desperate. That was a winter long to be remembered for its severity, and night after night my poor father would come in tired and wet with his little sack practically empty.

We were driven to eating prayer-books, and when those gave out we took to the Minister's sermons. That was, for me, the final straw. The prayer-books were tough, but those sermons!

Being the oldest, it seemed fitting that I should go out into the world and make my own way. Perhaps I could in some way help the others. At least, it left one less to be provided for.

So, saying farewell to all of them—my mother and father and all the children from Bathsheba to Zenas—I set forth on the coldest, windiest night of a cold and windy winter.

Little did I dream, at that moment, of all the strange people and experiences I should encounter before ever I returned to that little vestry home! All I thought of were my cold paws, my empty stomach—and those sermons.

J have never known
how far I traveled that night, for,
what with the cold and hunger, I
must have become slightly deliri-
ous. The first thing I remember
clearly was being in a kitchen and
smelling CHEESE! It didn't take
long to find it; it was only a bit of
rind and fairly dry, but how I ate!

Refreshed by this, my first real
meal in many a day, I began to explore the house. It was painfully
bare; clean, but bare. Very little
furniture, and that all hard and
shiny; no soft things, or dusty corners where a chap could curl up

and have a good warm nap. It was
cold too, almost as cold as outdoors.

Upstairs were two rooms. One
was dark, and from it came the
sound of snoring; the other had a
light, and the sound of sneezing. I
chose the sneezy one.

In a large chair close to the
fireplace sat a short, thick, round-
faced man, trying to write by the

light of a candle. Every few moments he would sneeze, and his square-rimmed glasses would fly off. Reaching for these he would drop his pen; by the time he found that and got settled to write, the candle would flicker from the draught; when that calmed down, the sneezing would start again, and so it went. He was not accomplishing much in the way of writing.

Of course I recognized him. Everyone in Philadelphia knew the great Doctor Benjamin Franklin, scientist, inventor, printer, editor, author, soldier, statesman and philosopher.

He didn't look great or famous that night, though, he just looked cold—and a bit silly.

He was wrapped in a sort of dressing-gown, with a dirty fur collar; and on his head was perched an odd-looking fur cap.

The cap interested me, for I was still chilled to the bone—and this room was just as bleak as the rest of the house. It was a rather disreputable-looking affair, that cap; but in one side of it I had spied a hole—just about my size.

Up the back of the chair I went, and under cover of the next fit of sneezes, in I slid. What a cozy place *that* was! Plenty of room to move about a bit; just enough air; such soft fur, and such warmth!

"Here," said I to myself, "is my home. No more cold streets, or cellars, or vestries. HERE I stay."

At the moment, of course, I never realized how true this was to prove. All I realized was that I was warm, well fed and—oh, so sleepy!

And so to bed.

341

WE INVENT THE FRANKLIN STOVE

I slept late the next morning. When I woke my fur-cap home was hanging on the bedpost, and I in it.

Dr. Franklin was again crouched over the fire attempting to write, between fits of sneezing and glasses-hunting. The fire, what there was of it, was smoking, and the room was as cold as ever.

"Not wishing to be critical—" I said. "But, perhaps, a bit of wood on that smoky ember that you seem to consider a fire might—"

"WASTE NOT, WANT NOT," said he, severe, and went on writing.

"Well, just suppose," I said, "just suppose you spend two or three weeks in bed with pewmonia—would that be a waste or—"

"It would be," said he, putting on a log; "whatever your name might be."

"Amos," said I. . . . "And then there'd be doctors' bills—"

"BILLS!" said he, shuddering, and put on two more logs, quick. The fire blazed up then, and the room became a little better, but not much.

"Dr. Franklin," I said, "that fireplace is all wrong."

"You might call me Ben—just plain Ben," said he. . . . "What's wrong with it?"

"Well, for one thing, most of the heat goes up the chimney. And for another, you can't get *around* it. Now, outside our church there used to be a Hot-chestnut Man. Sometimes, when business was rushing, he'd drop a chestnut. Pop was always on the look-out, and almost before it touched the ground he'd have it in his sack—and down to the vestry with it. There he'd put it in the middle of the floor—and we'd all gather round for the warmth.

"Twenty-eight of us it would heat, and the room as well. It was all because it was OUT IN THE OPEN, not stuck in a hole in the wall like that fireplace."

"Amos," he interrupts, excited, "there's an idea there! But we couldn't move the fire out into the middle of the room."

"We could if there were something to put it in, iron or something."

"But the smoke?" he objected.

"PIPE," said I, and curled up for another nap.

$\mathscr{I}$ didn't get it, though.
Ben rushed off downstairs,
came back with a great armful
of junk, dumped it on
the floor and was off
for more. No one could
have slept, not even a dormouse.
After a few trips he had a big pile
of things there. There were scraps
of iron, tin and wire. There were
a couple of old warming-pans, an

iron oven, three flatirons, six pot-lids, a wire birdcage and an anvil. There were saws, hammers, pincers, files, drills, nails, screws, bolts, bricks, sand, and an old broken sword.

He drew out a sort of plan and went to work. With the clatter he made there was no chance of a nap, so I helped all I could, picking up the nuts and screws and tools that he dropped—and his glasses.

Ben was a fair terror for work, once he was interested. It was almost noon before he stopped for a bit of rest. We looked over what had been done and it didn't look so bad—considering.

It was shaped much like a small fireplace set up on legs, with two iron doors on the front and a smoke pipe running from the back to the fireplace. He had taken the andirons out of the fireplace and boarded that up so we wouldn't lose any heat up the chimney.

Ben walked around looking at it, proud as could be, but worried.

"The floor," he says. "It's the floor that troubles me, Amos. With those short legs and that thin iron bottom, the heat—"

"Down on the docks," said I, "we used to hear the ship-rats telling how the sailors build their cooking fires on board ship. A layer of sand right on the deck, bricks on top of that, and—"

"Amos," he shouts, "you've got it!" and rushed for the bricks and sand. He put a layer of sand in the bottom of the affair, the bricks on top of that, and then set the andirons in.

It looked pretty promising.

"Eureka!" he exclaims, stepping back to admire it—and tripping over the saw. "Straighten things up a bit, Amos, while I run and get some logs."

"*Don't* try to run," I said. "And by the way, do you come through the pantry on the way up?"

"Why?" he asked.

"In some ways, Ben," I said, "you're fairly bright, but in others you're just plain dull. The joy of creating may be meat and drink to you; but as for me, a bit of cheese—"

He was gone before I finished, but when he came back with the logs he did have a fine slab of cheese, a loaf of rye bread, and a good big tankard of ale.

We put in some kindling and logs and lit her up. She drew fine, and Ben was so proud and excited that I had to be rather sharp with him before he would settle down to food. Even then he was up every minute, to admire it from a new angle.

Before we'd finished even one sandwich, the room had warmed up like a summer afternoon.

"Amos," says he, "we've done it!"

"Thanks for the WE," I said. "I'll remember it."

Meet

Robert Lawson

$\mathcal{R}$obert Lawson was trying to decide how to write a book about Ben Franklin. His wife happened to see a picture of Franklin and commented that Franklin's fur hat looked like "a rat's nest." That gave Lawson the idea to write *Ben and Me*, about a mouse who lived in Franklin's fur cap. Lawson named the character Amos, because the name sounds like "a mouse."

Ben and Me was the first book Lawson wrote, although he had already illustrated several others, including the children's classic *Ferdinand*, which is about a gentle bull. Lawson went on to write many other books on a wide range of subjects. In the process, he became the first person to win both a Caldecott Medal (for *They Were Strong and Good*) and a Newbery Medal (for *Rabbit Hill*).

Lawson illustrated his first book in 1930, and he died in 1957. During those twenty-seven years, he wrote and illustrated dozens of books. Many of them have become classics and are still popular today, including *Mr. Revere and I*, a book about Paul Revere told from the point of view of his horse.

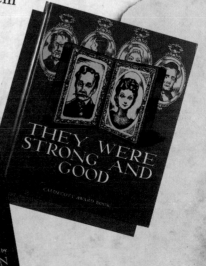

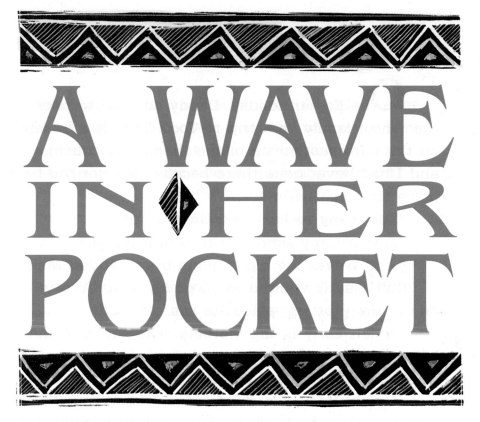

A WAVE IN HER POCKET

by Lynn Joseph · illustrated by Brian Pinkney

Almost all families in Trinidad have a tantie. A tantie is usually a grandaunt who helps to take care of all the grandnephews and grandnieces. She often gives advice to mothers on raising children even if she herself has no children. On family outings she entertains the children by gathering them all together and telling them stories. Sometimes she tells stories to teach them a lesson. Sometimes she tells stories to scare them or make them laugh. But the main thing about a tantie's stories is that she always has one ready, because any time is story time.

Many of the stories that tanties tell originate in the countries of West Africa. Others begin right in Trinidad. And some tanties make up stories that no one else has ever told before.

Here is one of my tantie's best stories, remembered forever.

It seemed like all this prettiness woke Tantie up. She stopped sitting still and started looking around. She looked out Susan's window and smiled at the trees and the sky. She looked out the front window and smiled at the next hill coming up. Then she looked out my window where the blue sea was shining in the sunlight, and her smile disappeared clean off her face.

"Tantie, what's wrong?" I asked.

Tantie just stared and stared at the sea. Then the strangest thing happened. A tear rolled down her face. It was just me who saw. I didn't know what to do. I put my head on Tantie's shoulder and squeezed her hand real tight.

Daddy drove up and down one hill after another. Each valley was prettier than the one before. I didn't look at Tantie anymore but I could feel her staring out my window.

Finally, we reached Toco. The first thing I saw as Daddy parked the car was a huge turtle walking on the sand. His head was out of his shell and he was looking all around. When he saw us, though, he stuck his head quick quick back in his shell and sat on the beach like a rock. Tantie saw this and laughed. I laughed too, 'cause I was happy to see Tantie not sad anymore. Cedric and Susan and Mama and Daddy started laughing also. When everybody else arrived they thought we were a bunch of crazies because we were sitting on the beach laughing at a rock.

After a while Mama and Daddy and Auntie Hazel and the rest of the family gathered the picnic baskets and climbed over the rocks to find a good place to eat. I decided to

"'Don't go,' she said in her mind. She looked in his eyes and saw de sea. And his smile was better than de sun. But she couldn't say her words out loud. She stepped back and let him go."

"How come she couldn't talk?" I asked, forgetting all about Tantie's shush finger. "Was she scared that Godfrey wouldn't listen to her?"

Tantie smiled slowly. "Yes, I think that's why. Anyway, let me tell de rest of de story.

"That afternoon Delphine waited and waited for Godfrey to come back. She climbed on top her high rock and shaded her eyes from de sun. She looked and looked, but she couldn't see anything but waves.

"De next afternoon Delphine climbed on top her rock again. She waited and waited. She even forgot to feed de turtles. But Godfrey still didn't come. Every day she climbed de rock and looked at de sea for Godfrey. But only de waves looked back at her. Then one day as she stood on her rock, Delphine thought she heard de waves singing a song.

> *"I'll marry my love, the deep blue sea,*
> *And carry him in my pocket.*
> *I'll marry my love*
> *And carry my love,*
> *A wonderful wave in my pocket."*

"Tantie, what that song mean? How can you carry a wave in your pocket?" I asked.

"That's what Delphine wondered, too," said Tantie. "She thought it was a song from Godfrey but she didn't know what it meant."

"Well, did she ever figure it out?" I asked, looking at the big waves splashing onto the sand.

Secret Talk

by Eve Merriam

I have a friend
and sometimes we meet
and greet each other
without a word.

We walk through a field
and stalk a bird
and chew a blade of
pungent grass.

We let time pass
for a golden hour
while we twirl a flower
of Queen Anne's lace

or find a lion's face
shaped in a cloud
that's drifting, sifting
across the sky.

There's no need to say,
"It's been a fine day"
when we say goodbye:
when we say goodbye
we just wave a hand
and we understand.

CONTENTS

364

WAY TO GO

It's good to have an end to journey towards, but it is the journey that matters, in the end.

URSULA K. LE GUIN

366

Meet
Delia Ray

Delia Ray knows first-hand the hardships of the Yukon. To research her book *Gold! The Klondike Adventure,* she traveled to White Horse, a small city in the heart of gold-rush country. There, she had planned to study historical photographs and papers in the local museum. But the museum was closed! Next, she got snowed in. "It helped me get a picture of what it must have been like for the early goldseekers," she says. Eventually, though, she spent a week in the government archives, poring over letters, Mounted Police records, and other documents dating back to 1897.

At the University of Washington in Seattle, Ray discovered a treasure-trove of photographs and accounts by people who had joined in the Klondike gold rush. "I began to think anybody who ever came back to Seattle wrote a book about the Klondike experience," she jokes.

"I loved looking at the old Klondike photos," recalls Ray. "Some were taken in people's cabins, . . . usually by photographers who knew the people involved. The book really began with the photos."

KLONDIKE
Fever

by Delia Ray

George Washington Carmack

Skookum Jim

Tagish Charley

The city of Seattle was usually still asleep at daybreak on weekend mornings, but this Saturday large crowds of people rushed to the downtown waterfront at dawn. They shouted excitedly to one another, pointed across the water, and craned their necks to see. The *Portland* was coming! With its smokestack puffing and whistle blowing, the steamship chugged its way toward shore. On board was the most precious cargo ever to enter the Seattle harbor—sixty-eight miners from the Klondike and more than two tons of gold.

It was two days earlier when the first of the gold ships had arrived in San Francisco, California. The steamer *Excelsior* had sailed into port, bringing its load of gold and the news that an even richer treasure ship was on its way to Seattle. Finally, the *Portland* appeared in Seattle on July 17, 1897—almost one year after George Washington Carmack and his close friends Tagish Charley and Skookum Jim made their discovery on Bonanza Creek.

To the impatient spectators on the dock, the *Portland* seemed to move in slow motion. "Show us the gold!" yelled the onlookers, and several miners on board lifted their heavy sacks for all to see. A thrill swept through the crowd, as each person imagined the glittering gold dust and nuggets inside the bags.

The big ship carefully pulled alongside the wharf and the gangplank was lowered.

When the first miner stepped into full view, the people stared in amazement. He heaved a buckskin bag to his shoulder and steadied the load. His face was lean and weather-beaten, lined with the strain of hard work and long Yukon winters. Behind him two men staggered down the ramp, each grasping the end of a sagging blanket. One after another they came, carrying old leather suitcases, pine boxes, and pickle jars—anything that would hold the heavy piles of gold. The commotion on the docks grew with each miner that appeared. "Hurray for the Klondike!" the people cried.

As the ragged and bearded men set foot on shore, they squinted into the crowd, searching for familiar faces. Instead of old friends and relatives,

The passengers of the Portland *arrived in Seattle with over two tons of gold and fantastic stories of the rich Klondike. Several of the miners in this photograph rest their sacks of gold on their shoulders.*

Newspaper headlines reflected the excitement created by the arrival of the Portland.

they were greeted by throngs of reporters eager for the story of the Golden North. Most of the miners tried to escape the newsmen with their persistent questions and headed for the best restaurant they could find. They ordered huge feasts with fresh fruit and vegetables, for many had been living on a diet of beans and flapjacks for months.

One of the reporters' favorite front page subjects was Clarence Berry, who had stepped off the *Portland* with $130,000 in gold nuggets. With his magnificent strength and honest ways, the broad-shouldered miner instantly became Seattle's hero. Berry had set out from California to find his fortune three years earlier, leaving behind his childhood sweetheart and a bankrupt fruit farm. When he reached Alaska, Berry joined forty other anxious goldseekers bound for the Yukon. The long winter journey over the mountains was harsh, and many in the group gave up in despair. More turned back when a fierce storm whipped up, destroying all of their supplies, but Berry pressed on. Of the forty goldseekers who began

the trip, only he and two other men reached their final destination.

As the newspapers reported, Berry was not discouraged when he did not strike gold during his first year in the Klondike. He returned to California only long enough to marry his sweetheart, Ethyl Bush. Then back to the Yukon he went, with his new wife wrapped in a fur robe and bearskin hood.

Berry was working as a bartender in the saloon at the town of Forty Mile when George Carmack entered with his shotgun shell full of gold dust. Berry threw down his apron and joined the stampede to the Klondike goldfields. Before long he had hired twenty-five workmen to help harvest the riches from his claim on Eldorado Creek. The gold lay thick, so thick that Mrs. Berry—as *The Seattle Times* reported—could walk through the diggings and pick up nuggets "as easily as a hen picks up grains of corn in a barnyard." In one season she gathered more than $10,000 in nuggets during her occasional strolls through the claim.

After the solitude of a rustic cabin in the North, the Berrys were not prepared for the swarms of reporters and followers that trailed them into restaurants and surrounded them on the street. The couple fled to San Francisco, but the crowds were just as curious there. The callers lined up outside the Berrys' room at the Grand Hotel, until finally Mr. Berry allowed them to enter. Inside Room 111 was a glittering exhibition of gold. The visitors marveled over nuggets as big as chicken eggs and glass bottles full of gold dust, each labeled with the worth it contained.

In Seattle the excitement had reached a state of frenzy. The streets were packed with people

A group of businessmen proudly display one and one-half tons of gold at the Alaska Commercial Company office in the Klondike. At today's prices, this amount would be worth well over ten million dollars.

who rushed downtown to celebrate the news from the North. Large groups gathered at banks and shop windows, where stacks of gold bricks and piles of shining nuggets were on display. One could not walk down the street without hearing the word *Klondike* spoken in a dozen different conversations.

The reason for this wild excitement was simple: The Klondike gold ships arrived during a time of terrible poverty for the United States. Thousands of businesses were closing, and millions of people had lost their jobs. It was not unusual to see a man die of hunger in the streets or a family pushed out of its home because of unpaid bills. This period of hardship, known as an economic depression, had lasted for several years and it seemed that it would never end.

The arrival of the *Portland* and the *Excelsior* was like a dream come true for the poverty-stricken nation. Penniless men read with delight each new tale of wealth in the daily papers. They read about William Stanley, who left Seattle as a poor bookshop owner and returned a millionaire. Now Stanley's wife could quit her job as a laundry-woman and order a whole new wardrobe of fancy clothes. They read about Tom Lippy, a former athletic instructor. He and his wife brought back $60,000 in gold—a fortune in 1897, when a full meal could be purchased for 25 cents. Everywhere, people were certain they could make a trip to the Yukon and strike it rich, just as William Stanley and Tom Lippy had.

The Klondike gold rush was on. "THE POPULATION IS PREPARING TO MOVE TO THE KLONDIKE" shouted the newspaper headlines.

"EVERY MAN SEEMS TO HAVE CAUGHT THE KLONDIKE FEVER." Within hours after the gold ships had sailed into harbor, many men and women were quitting their jobs and preparing to head north. Seattle streetcar workers abandoned their trolleys on the track. Nuns left their churches, and a quarter of the police force resigned. Even the mayor announced his resignation and promptly bought a steamboat for carrying passengers to the Klondike.

Firemen, store clerks, school teachers, lawyers, and doctors—workers from Seattle to San Francisco decided to trade their regular paychecks for picks and shovels. But the West Coast of the United States was not the only region to be turned upside down by the Yukon discoveries. "Klondike fever" had spread to cities and towns throughout the country—and throughout the world. In New York, 2,000 people tried to buy tickets for the Klondike before the news of the gold strikes was one day old. Soon, groups of fortune hunters from Australia, Scotland, England, France, Italy, and other countries were also making their way toward the Yukon.

Many people could not afford to buy the steamship ticket or the supplies needed to travel northward. However, there were other ways for a poor, but determined, man to join the gold rush. Often a more wealthy acquaintance, who could not make the trip himself, was willing to provide a "grubstake"—the money needed to buy provisions for the journey. In return, the Klondiker had to promise that he would pay his debt with a share of whatever gold he found.

Eager to reach Dawson, the Klondike "City of Gold," many goldseekers hastily built sailboats such as the Yukon Flyer.

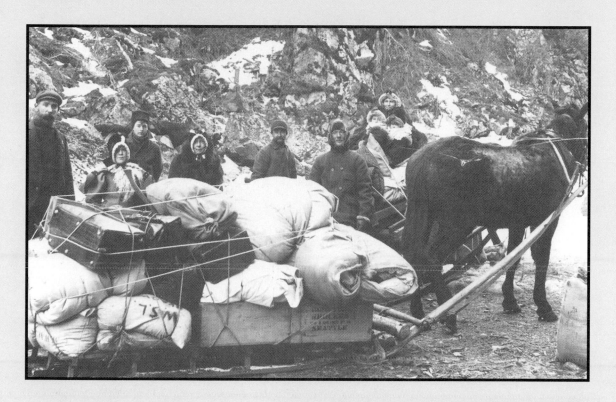

The hardware stores and grocery counters were booming with business. In Seattle, San Francisco, and other West Coast port cities, gold-seekers jammed store aisles. Never had shopping lists been so carefully prepared. Each Klondiker wanted to face the Arctic winds and long journey ahead with the warmest clothes and most nourishing food that money could buy.

By the winter of 1897, Canadian government officials had passed a law forbidding anyone from entering the goldfields without enough supplies to last an entire year. Once a prospector had spent $500 to buy a year's worth of goods for the Klondike, his load weighed about 2,000 pounds. Many newspapers and guidebooks printed checklists of the exact items needed for a proper outfit, as the miners called their store of provisions.

Not only hardened miners and strong men followed the dangerous Klondike trails. As this photograph shows, entire families—even grandmothers and small children—joined the rush over White Pass.

377

These were just some of the supplies that the future prospectors took along:

flour (150 pounds)   1 frying pan
bacon (150 pounds)   1 coffee pot
beans (100 pounds)   11 bars of soap
dried apples (25 pounds)   1 tin of matches
dried peaches (25 pounds)   1 box of candles
dried apricots (25 pounds)   1 medicine chest
rice (25 pounds)   1 pick
butter (25 pounds)   1 shovel
granulated sugar (100 pounds)   1 ax
coffee (15 pounds)   1 gold pan
tea (10 pounds)   1 handsaw
salt (10 pounds)   1 hatchet
pepper (1 pound)   6 towels
vinegar (1 gallon)   1 sheet-iron stove
1 tent   nails (16 pounds)

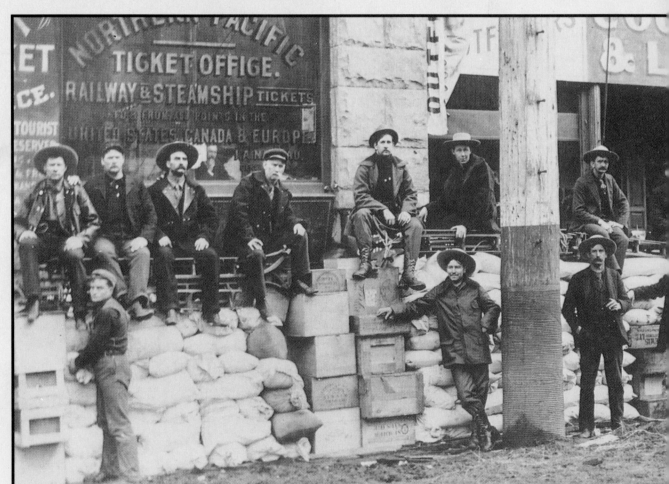

As the Klondikers waited for their hour of departure, they proudly sauntered up and down the streets in their new iron-toed boots and plaid flannel shirts. By now they were used to the scenes of confusion around them. The sidewalks were piled ten feet high with sacks of flour and crates of mining equipment ready to be sold to the next wave of stampeders. Long lines of people formed outside steamship offices, where the tickets were quickly sold out and clerks turned away hundreds of disappointed goldseekers. Dogs of every breed—huskies, Labradors, Saint Bernards, and golden retrievers—ran barking through the streets with their owners chasing after them. Dogs had suddenly become very valuable possessions, for many

In Seattle many merchants made fortunes selling equipment to goldseekers. Here, a group of future miners, ready to set out for the Klondike, stand in front of a wall of flour sacks and mining supplies.

Many businesses profited from the world's fascination with the Klondike. Eager fortune hunters paid the Yukon Mining School for lessons in driving dog teams, panning for gold, and using sluiceboxes.

would be trained to haul sleds full of supplies over the Klondike snow.

The stampeders often paused to watch street salesmen show off the newest products designed for those traveling north. There were Klondike medicine chests, Klondike blankets, and Klondike electric gold pans. There were portable Klondike houses, which the peddlers told their customers were "as light as air," even with the double bed and special Yukon stove that folded up inside. Dried food was sold in large quantities to future miners who wanted to save weight and space in their backpacks. Although most of the food was colorless and tasted bad, the miners bought everything from dried onions and turnips to evaporated rhubarb and potatoes.

Many dishonest merchants made money during the gold rush by selling worthless products or taking advantage of the innocent goldseekers. One Klondiker, Arthur Dietz, stopped on the street to watch a salesman pour some yellow powder from a sack and make a plate of scrambled eggs. Dietz was so impressed that he bought 100 pounds of the evaporated eggs for him and his traveling companions. It was not until the group was well on its way to the Klondike that Dietz opened the sacks. He realized that the yellow powder inside was really not eggs at all. The

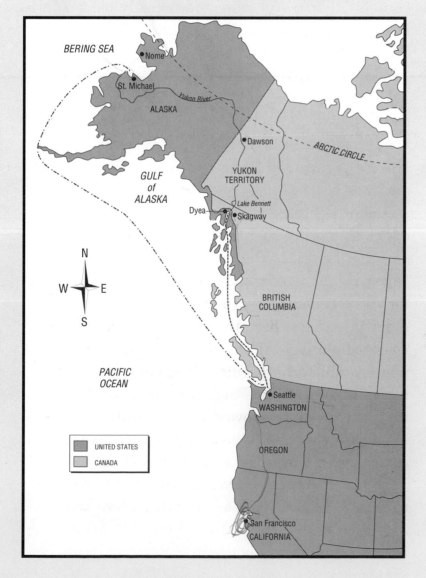

This map shows the two most popular routes to the Klondike—the Inside Passage, which led goldseekers through Dyea or Skagway, and the All-Water Route through St. Michael and up the Yukon River to Dawson. While Seattle was the world's busiest Klondike port, stampeders also set out for Dawson from other major harbors along the West Coast.

deceitful salesman had switched sacks and sold him 100 pounds of corn meal.

Like Arthur Dietz, thousands of goldseekers would face many unexpected difficulties on the Klondike trail. Most of the fortune hunters rushed to buy their tickets without truly knowing where their journey would lead them or what obstacles lay ahead. They read guidebooks about the Klondike, but even these were often inaccurate and misleading. Several books told readers that the Klondike was located in Alaska, when actually the region lay just across the Canadian border. Other travel guides incorrectly led readers to believe that the trails to the Klondike were like winding country lanes.

Many people also had unrealistic ideas of what their lives would be like once they reached the Klondike. One man set out for the Yukon as if he were taking a pleasant northern vacation. His outfit included thirty-two pairs of moccasins, one case of pipes, two Irish setters, a puppy, and a badminton set. Another man, who worked as a dance instructor, had hopes that he could give dancing lessons to the miners and Indians of the North, while digging nuggets during his spare time in the summer. A woman from Ireland planned to move her entire family to the Yukon, where she imagined her sons and daughters would attend school in the daytime and dig gold in the early mornings and late evenings. None of these Klondikers expected the harsh Arctic climate or understood that, to make any money, gold digging had to be a full-time job.

No one had more impractical ideas of how to become wealthy in the Klondike than the

businessmen, scientists, and inventors of the day. The newspapers were full of advertisements for strange new inventions that were "guaranteed" to make gold mining easier and pockets fuller. A business called the Trans-Alaskan Gopher Company promised to train gophers to claw through the icy gravel and uncover nuggets of gold.

Another scheme was the "Klondike Bicycle." Its inventor, Jacob Coxey, told reporters that his special bike could carry 500 pounds of supplies all the way to the Yukon. With its unfolding side-wheels, handlebar attachments, and rawhide-bound frame, the unsuccessful Klondike Bicycle was a comical looking vehicle. Certainly, if Jacob Coxey had ever seen the Yukon's steep mountains

In the early days of the gold rush, many newcomers arrived in Dawson expecting to find a wealthy town with tidy shops and clean streets. Instead, they found confusion and rivers of mud.

As steam from the ship's boilers fills the air, passengers look down on hundreds of friends, relatives, and spectators who jam the docks, waiting to see the *Humboldt* leave for the Klondike.

and dense forests, he never would have invented such an odd contraption.

As the summer of 1897 passed, a new ship left for the Klondike almost every day. The gold-seekers boarded the most unusual assortment of boats ever assembled. Coal ships, yachts, schooners, barges, and old fishing boats—any vessel that could float became a gold ship. Many boats that had long ago been declared unsafe were quickly brought in from the shipyards. Even with the hasty repairs that were made, many Klondike boats were referred to as "floating coffins."

Despite warnings, the excited stampeders did not seem to care whether their boats were seaworthy or not. The gold-crazed people pushed up the ramps, filling every available space on board. Passengers stood elbow-to-elbow. Over the ships' railings, several tearful faces appeared. Many goldseekers would not see their families again for months and months. But as the crowd below cried, "Three cheers for the Klondike!" and the ship whistles blasted a farewell, most of the passengers forgot their sadness.

Their Klondike adventure had finally begun.

As stampeders confidently set out on untraveled routes to the Klondike, a transformation took place in the North. On their way to Dawson, many stampeders discovered fertile ground for farming. Others stumbled upon creeks showing traces of gold. Men and women cut their journeys short and stayed to develop the land. As if a hidden door had been flung open, the mystery surrounding Alaska and northwest Canada disappeared. Suddenly, the North was a frontier for opportunity.

Few mining fortunes were made in the Klondike. In the early days comforts were rare and hardships were common. Yet, most of those who took part in this strange mass movement northward continued to share one special thought until they died: they would not have missed the Klondike adventure for anything in the world.

Thousands of men and women returned to their normal lives after the Klondike gold rush, but their outlook on the world had changed profoundly. The stampede taught those who reached Dawson that they could survive hardships and make a home in a desolate land—achievements that had seemed impossible only a few months before.

from Song of the Open Road

Afoot and light-hearted I take to the open road,
Healthy, free, the world before me,
The long brown path before me leading wherever I
    choose.

Henceforth I ask not good-fortune, I myself am
    good-fortune,
Henceforth I whimper no more, postpone no more,
    need nothing,
Done with indoor complaints, libraries, querulous
    criticisms,
Strong and content I travel the open road.

Walt Whitman

Arkville Landscape by Alexander H. Wyant

Although Walt Whitman (1819–1892) wrote poetry and Alexander H. Wyant (1836–1892) created paintings, a love of nature is apparent in the work of both artists.

Meet Virginia Hamilton

The House of Dies Drear was inspired by a part of Virginia Hamilton's family history that was "so secret, it took my mother a long time to tell even me about it," she says. Hamilton's grandfather, Levi Perry, was a slave who "had traveled through the secret Underground Railroad from the state of Virginia (thus my name)" to the town of Yellow Springs, Ohio, where Hamilton grew up. Along the way, he had been helped by the abolitionist John Rankin. Rankin's house in Ripley, Ohio—like many others in the area—had provided runaway slaves with a safe hiding place as they fled north toward freedom. Those houses also provided Hamilton with material for her story.

The research Hamilton did for the book deepened her respect for her grandfather and for others who risked so much for freedom. Hamilton describes writing *The House of Dies Drear* as "my way of paying tribute to my roots." The book has won several awards and was dramatized on the television program "Wonderworks." A chapter from another of Hamilton's novels, *Willie Bea and the Time the Martians Landed*, appears in Unit 6.

The House of Dies Drear

by Virginia Hamilton
illustrated by Thomas Blackshear

There was gray light filtering down from the opening of the steps to where Thomas lay, and he could see that he was at the edge of a steep stairway cut out of rock. The stairs were wet; he could hear water dripping down on them from somewhere.

"I could have rolled down those steps," he whispered. Mac Darrow and Pesty must have known there was a drop down to where Thomas now lay. But they hadn't told him. "They are not friends then," said Thomas softly. He cautioned himself to be more careful.

I was showing off, he thought. I hurried and I fell. That was just what they'd wanted.

"Move slowly. Think fast," Thomas whispered. "Keep in mind what's behind and look closely at what's in front."

Thomas always carried a pencil-thin flashlight, which he sometimes used for reading in the car. He sat up suddenly and pulled out the flashlight. It wasn't broken from the fall, and he flicked it on. He sat in a kind of circle enclosed by brick walls. In some places, the brick had crumbled into powder, which was slowly filling up the circle of sod.

That will take a long time, thought Thomas. He looked up at the underside of the veranda steps.

Thomas got to his feet and made his way down the rock stairway into darkness. At the foot of the stairs was a path with walls of dirt and rock on either side of it. The walls were so close, Thomas could touch them by extending his arms a few inches. Above his head was a low ceiling carved out of rock. Such cramped space made him uneasy. The foundation of the house had to be somewhere above the natural rock. The idea of the whole three-story house of Dies Drear pressing down on him caused him to stop a moment on the path. Since he had fallen, he hadn't had time to be afraid. He wasn't now, but he did begin to worry a little about where the path led. He thought of ghosts, and yet he did not seriously

pounded on it, hurting himself more, causing his head to spin. He kept on, because he knew he was about to be taken from behind by something ghostly and cold.

"Help me! It's going to get me!" he called. "Help me!"

Thomas heard a high, clear scream on the other side of the wall. Next came the sound of feet scurrying, and then the wall slid silently up.

"Thomas Small!" his mother said. "What in heaven's name do you think you are doing inside that wall!"

"I see you've found yourself a secret passage," said Mr. Small. "I hadn't thought you'd find that button by the front door so soon."

Mr. Small, with Billy and Buster, was seated at the kitchen table. They were finishing supper. Mr. Small smiled at Thomas, while the twins stared at him with solemn eyes.

Mrs. Small stood directly in front of Thomas and then stepped aside so that he could take a few steps into the kitchen. Thomas glanced behind him at the tunnel, a gaping space carved out of the comfortable kitchen. He saw nothing at all on the path.

He sat down beside his father. There was the good smell of food hanging in the air. The twins seemed full and content.

"You knew about that tunnel, Papa?" Thomas said. He felt discouraged, as though he'd been tricked.

"If anyone came unexpectedly to the front door," said Mr. Small, "the slaves could hide in the tunnel until whoever it was had gone. Or, if and when the callers began a search, the slaves could escape through the kitchen or by way of the veranda steps."

It's not any fun, Thomas thought. Not if he already knows about it.

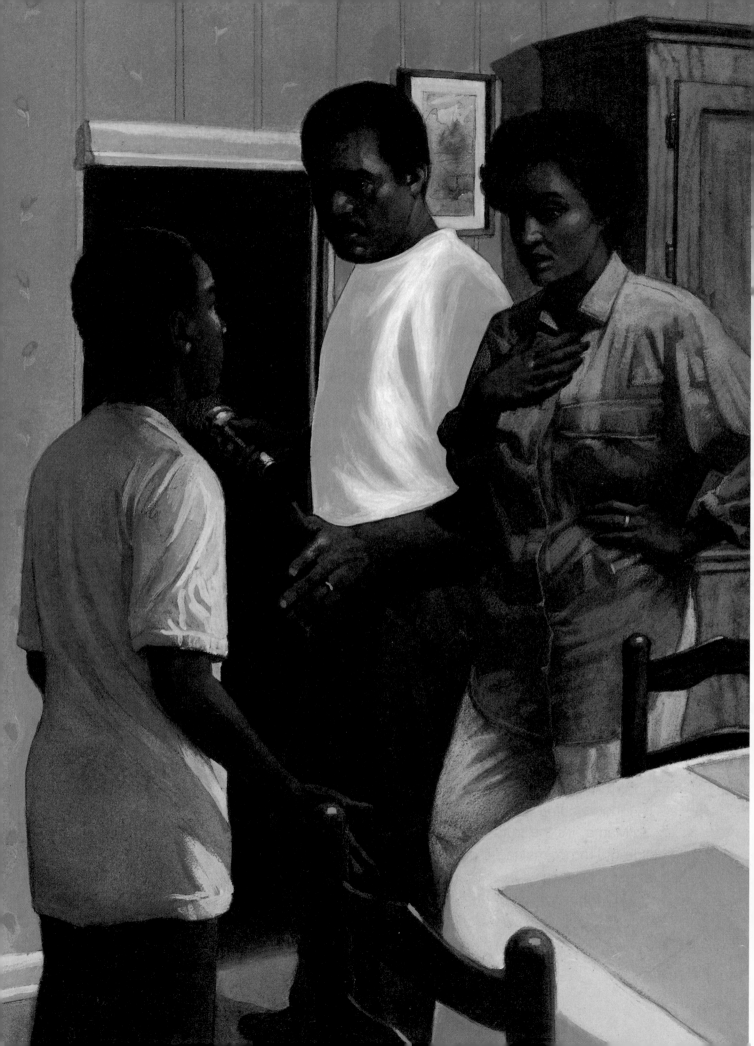

"Yes, they came from around the house just after I found the button and moved the steps." Then Thomas told all about Pesty, the horse and Mac Darrow. He even managed to make his father and mother understand that the children had been playing with him, toying with him, as if he were the object of a game.

"They were not friends," Thomas said finally. "They let me fall under those steps."

"No, they weren't if they did let you fall," said his mother, "but maybe they didn't know about that drop down."

"No," said Mr. Small, "they probably knew, but I would guess they had no real intention of causing Thomas harm. It was their joke on the 'new boy.' It wasn't a very nice joke and it was a joke that might have not worked at all. They were playing with you, Thomas, to find out what you knew. They must have thought you knew more than they did. After all, you came from far away to live in a house that no child in his right mind in these parts would dare enter. I would think that by now you are pretty famous all over town."

"I see," said Thomas. "Because I dared go into 'Mr. Pluto's tunnel'!"

"Yes," his father said.

"It wasn't a human voice I heard," Thomas said. "It wasn't alive."

They all fell silent for a moment. Then Mr. Small asked, "And you're sure you heard nothing more than that sighing?"

"That's all," Thomas said. "It just kept coming at me, getting closer."

Mr. Small got up and stood at the tunnel opening. He went into the long hall after a few seconds and came back with a flashlight. "I'll go with you," Thomas said.

"I'd rather you stayed here. I'll only be a minute," said his father.

Mr. Small was gone less than a minute. Thomas and his mother waited, staring into the tunnel opening, flooded with the light from the kitchen. A few feet beyond the opening, the

JUST AROUND THE CORNER

THE MYSTERY OF DREAR HOUSE
by Virginia Hamilton
Collier, 1988

The Drear house seen from the hill-top reminded him of a giant crow frozen on its nest. He wasn't sure yet whether he liked living in that house. He was usually on his guard. Sometimes he felt something strange was near. Something unseen but listening behind the walls, he thought.

GOING PLACES: THE YOUNG TRAVELER'S GUIDE AND ACTIVITY BOOK
by Harriet Webster
illustrated by Gail Owens
Aladdin, 1991

Where Do Places Get Their Names?
What Do I Do If I Get Lost?
Why Can't We Touch the Art?
Where Do Zoos Get Their Animals?

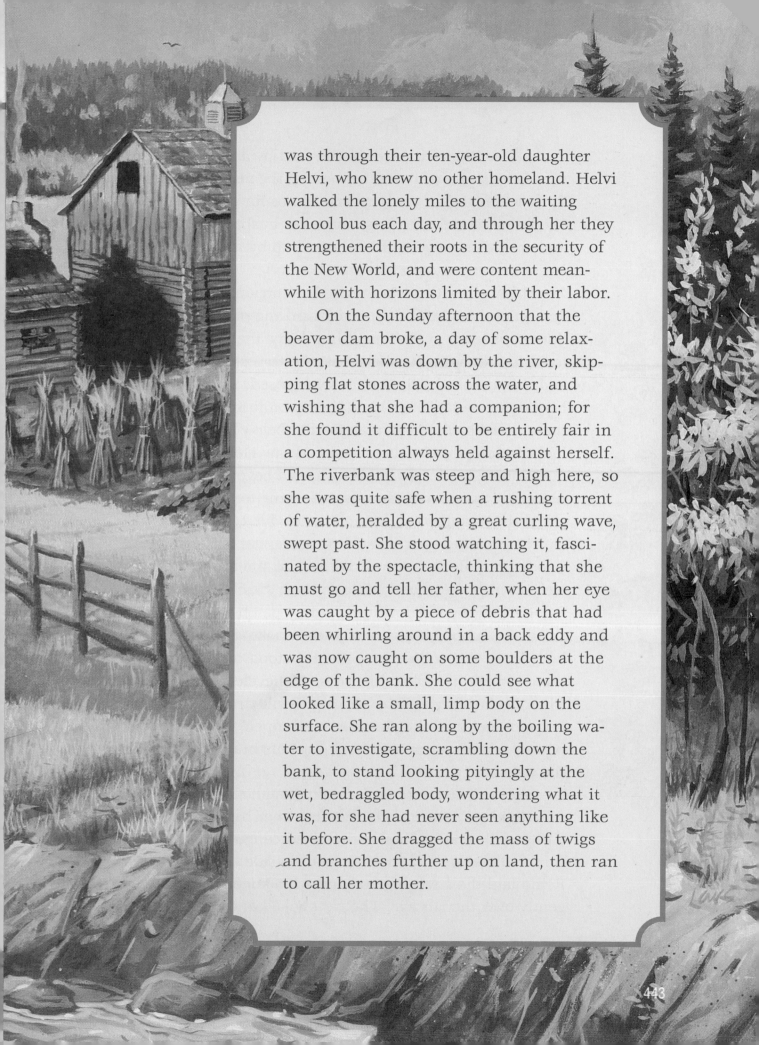

was through their ten-year-old daughter Helvi, who knew no other homeland. Helvi walked the lonely miles to the waiting school bus each day, and through her they strengthened their roots in the security of the New World, and were content meanwhile with horizons limited by their labor.

On the Sunday afternoon that the beaver dam broke, a day of some relaxation, Helvi was down by the river, skipping flat stones across the water, and wishing that she had a companion; for she found it difficult to be entirely fair in a competition always held against herself. The riverbank was steep and high here, so she was quite safe when a rushing torrent of water, heralded by a great curling wave, swept past. She stood watching it, fascinated by the spectacle, thinking that she must go and tell her father, when her eye was caught by a piece of debris that had been whirling around in a back eddy and was now caught on some boulders at the edge of the bank. She could see what looked like a small, limp body on the surface. She ran along by the boiling water to investigate, scrambling down the bank, to stand looking pityingly at the wet, bedraggled body, wondering what it was, for she had never seen anything like it before. She dragged the mass of twigs and branches further up on land, then ran to call her mother.

That night the Nurmis were having
fresh pickerel, cooked in the old-country
way with the head still on and surrounded
by potatoes. Helvi ladled the head with
some broth and potatoes into a saucer and
put it on the floor. Soon the fishhead had
disappeared to the accompaniment of
pleased rumbling growls. The potatoes followed; then, holding down the plate with
his paw, the cat polished it clean. Satisfied
at last, he stretched superbly, his front paws
extended so that he looked like a heraldic
lion, then jumped onto Helvi's lap, curled
himself around and purred loudly.

The parents' acceptance was completed
by his action, though there had never before been a time or place in the economy
of their lives for an animal which did not
earn its keep, or lived anywhere else except
the barn or kennel. For the first time in
her life Helvi had a pet.

Helvi carried the cat up to bed with
her, and he draped himself with familiar
ease over her shoulder as she climbed the
steep ladder stairs leading up to her little
room in the eaves. She tucked him tenderly
into an old wooden cradle, and he lay in
sleepy contentment, his dark face incon-
gruous against a doll's pillow.

Late in the night she woke to a loud
purring in her ear, and felt him treading a
circle at her back. The wind blew a gust of
cold rain across her face and she leaned

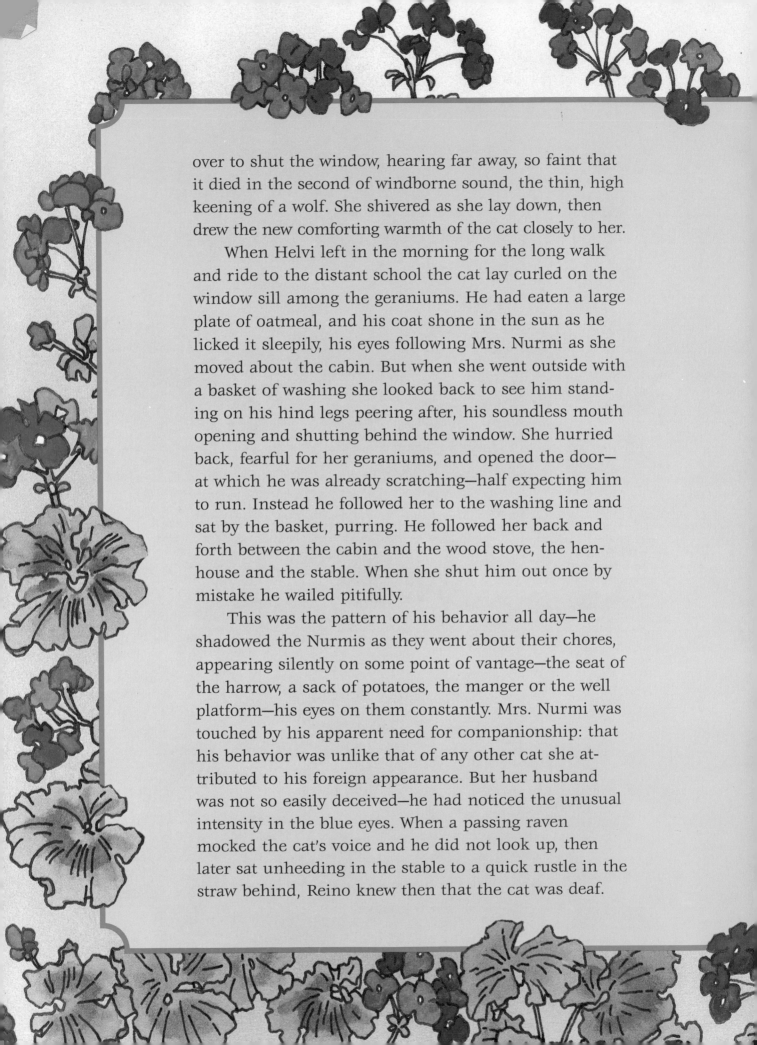

over to shut the window, hearing far away, so faint that it died in the second of windborne sound, the thin, high keening of a wolf. She shivered as she lay down, then drew the new comforting warmth of the cat closely to her.

When Helvi left in the morning for the long walk and ride to the distant school the cat lay curled on the window sill among the geraniums. He had eaten a large plate of oatmeal, and his coat shone in the sun as he licked it sleepily, his eyes following Mrs. Nurmi as she moved about the cabin. But when she went outside with a basket of washing she looked back to see him standing on his hind legs peering after, his soundless mouth opening and shutting behind the window. She hurried back, fearful for her geraniums, and opened the door—at which he was already scratching—half expecting him to run. Instead he followed her to the washing line and sat by the basket, purring. He followed her back and forth between the cabin and the wood stove, the hen-house and the stable. When she shut him out once by mistake he wailed pitifully.

This was the pattern of his behavior all day—he shadowed the Nurmis as they went about their chores, appearing silently on some point of vantage—the seat of the harrow, a sack of potatoes, the manger or the well platform—his eyes on them constantly. Mrs. Nurmi was touched by his apparent need for companionship: that his behavior was unlike that of any other cat she attributed to his foreign appearance. But her husband was not so easily deceived—he had noticed the unusual intensity in the blue eyes. When a passing raven mocked the cat's voice and he did not look up, then later sat unheeding in the stable to a quick rustle in the straw behind, Reino knew then that the cat was deaf.

Carrying her schoolbooks and lunch pail, Helvi
ran most of the way home across the fields and picked
up the cat as well when he came to meet her. He clung
to her shoulder, balancing easily, while she performed
the routine evening chores that awaited her. Undeterred
by his weight she fed the hens, gathered eggs, fetched
water, then sat at the table stringing dried mushrooms.
When she put him down before supper she saw that
her father was right—the pointed ears did not respond
to any sound, though she noticed that he started and
turned his head at the vibration if she clapped her
hands or dropped even a small pebble on the bare floor.

She had brought home two books from the traveling library, and after the supper dishes had been
cleared away her parents sat by the stove in the short
interval before bed while she read aloud to them, trans-
lating as she went. They sat, in their moment of rare
relaxation, with the cat stretched out on his back at
their feet, and the child's soft voice, flowing through
the dark austerity of the cabin, carried them beyond
the circle of light from the oil lamp to the warmth and
brightness of strange lands. . . .

They heard of seafaring Siamese cats who worked
their passages the world over, their small hammocks
made and slung by their human messmates, who held
them second to none as ship's cats; and of the great
proud Siamese Ratting Corps who patrolled the dock-
yards of Le Havre with unceasing vigilance; they saw,
with eyes withdrawn and dreaming, the palace watch-
cats of long-ago Siam, walking delicately on long
simian legs around the fountained courtyards, their
softly padding feet polishing the mosaics to a lustred
path of centuries. And at last they learned how these

nobly born Siamese acquired the kink at the end of their tails and bequeathed it to all their descendants.

And as they listened, they looked down in wonder, for there on the rag rug lay one of these, stretched out flat on his royal back, his illustrious tail twitching idly, and his jeweled eyes on their daughter's hand as she turned the pages that spoke of his ancestors—the guardian cats of the Siamese princesses. Each princess, when she came down to bathe in the palace lake, would slip her rings for safekeeping on the tail of her attendant cat. So zealous in their charge were these proud cats that they bent the last joint sideways for safer custody, and in time the faithful tails became crooked forever, and their children's and their children's children. . . .

One after another the Nurmis passed their hands admiringly down the tail before them to feel the truth in its bent bony tip; then Helvi gave him a bowl of milk, which he drank with regal condescension before she carried him up the ladder to bed.

That night, and for one more, the cat lay curled peacefully in Helvi's arms, and in the daytime during her absence he followed her parents everywhere. He trailed through the bush after her mother as she searched for late mushrooms, then sat on the cabin steps and patted the dropped corn kernels as she shucked a stack of cobs. He followed Reino and his work horse across the fields to the wood lot and perched on a newly felled pungent stump, his head following their every movement, and he curled by the door of the stable and watched the man mending harness and oiling traps. And in the late afternoons when Helvi returned he was there waiting for her, a rare and beautiful enigma in the certain routine of the day. He was one of them.

But on the fourth night he was restless, shaking his head and pawing his ears, his voice distressed at her back. At last he lay down, purring loudly, and pushed his head into her hand—the fur below his ears was soaking. She saw their sharp black triangles outlined against the little square of window and watched them flicker and quiver in response to every small night sound. Glad for him in his new-found hearing, she fell asleep.

When she woke, later in the night, aware of a lost warmth, she saw him crouched at the open window, looking out over the pale fields and the tall, dark trees below. His long sinuous tail thrashed to and fro as he measured the distance to the ground. Even as her hand moved out impulsively towards him he sprang, landing with a soft thud.

She looked down and saw his head turn for the first time to her voice, his eyes like glowing rubies as they caught the moonlight, then turn away— and with sudden desolate knowledge she knew that he had no further need of her. Through a blur of tears, she watched him go, stealing like a wraith in the night towards the river that had brought him. Soon the low swiftly running form was lost among the shadows.

Meet Sheila Burnford

The three animal travelers in *The Incredible Journey* might seem like odd companions, but the author, Sheila Burnford, had three pets just like them. Born in Scotland, Burnford moved to Canada with her family after World War II. She brought along a bull terrier named Bill. In Canada, a Siamese cat named Simon joined the family. Later, Burnford's husband bought a Labrador retriever, and the trio was complete.

Burnford was amazed at how well the three animals got along. Bill and Simon even slept in the same basket! Burnford noticed that her pets seemed to show concern for each other. They also seemed able to communicate. As Bill got older, his eyesight worsened. Burnford recalled that the Labrador began to go everywhere with the terrier, "waiting patiently at every place of interest, steering him back on the sidewalk when he would have strayed onto the road. . . ." Their friendship gave her the idea for *The Incredible Journey.*

Burnford's prizewinning novel has been translated into sixteen languages and was made into a movie. Burnford, who died in 1984, also wrote autobiographical stories, articles, and the children's book *Mr. Noah and the Second Flood.*

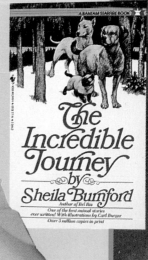

The Old Walking Song

by J. R. R. TOLKIEN

The Road goes ever on and on

Down from the door where it began.

Now far ahead the Road has gone,

And I must follow, if I can,

Pursuing it with eager feet,

Until it joins some larger way

Where many paths and errands meet.

And whither then? I cannot say.

CONTENTS

Are You Sure?

The important thing is to not
stop questioning.

ALBERT EINSTEIN

HOW to THiNK

ANSWERING QUESTIONS BY

LiKe a SciENtiST

THE SCIENTIFIC METHOD

by Stephen P. Kramer

illustrated by Kim Behm

WHUMP!!

"Whump, whump" went the tires of Pete's bike. The sounds were so close together they seemed like one noise.

"Hey!" screamed Pete. He pointed to the side of the road. "Look out! Get over!"

Jim could barely see the outline of Pete's arm in the darkness, but he swerved to the left. He coasted along the shoulder of the road until he caught up with Pete. Pete had stopped and was looking back.

"What's wrong?" asked Jim.

Pete shook his head. "A snake! A huge snake . . . I rode over it! On the side of the road! I didn't see it until too late . . . I couldn't even turn."

"Probably just an old inner tube," said Jim. "Come on, let's go."

"Was not," replied Pete, shaking his head again. "Want to go back and see?"

Jim hesitated for a moment. "All right," he answered. "I'm not scared."

Pete unhooked the flashlight from the frame of his bike. The boys laid their bicycles in the weeds beside the road and slowly walked back. The flashlight made a faint yellow spot on the pavement.

Pete shone the flashlight far ahead. "Up there," he said. "That's where I rode over it."

Jim looked around. "I don't see anything."

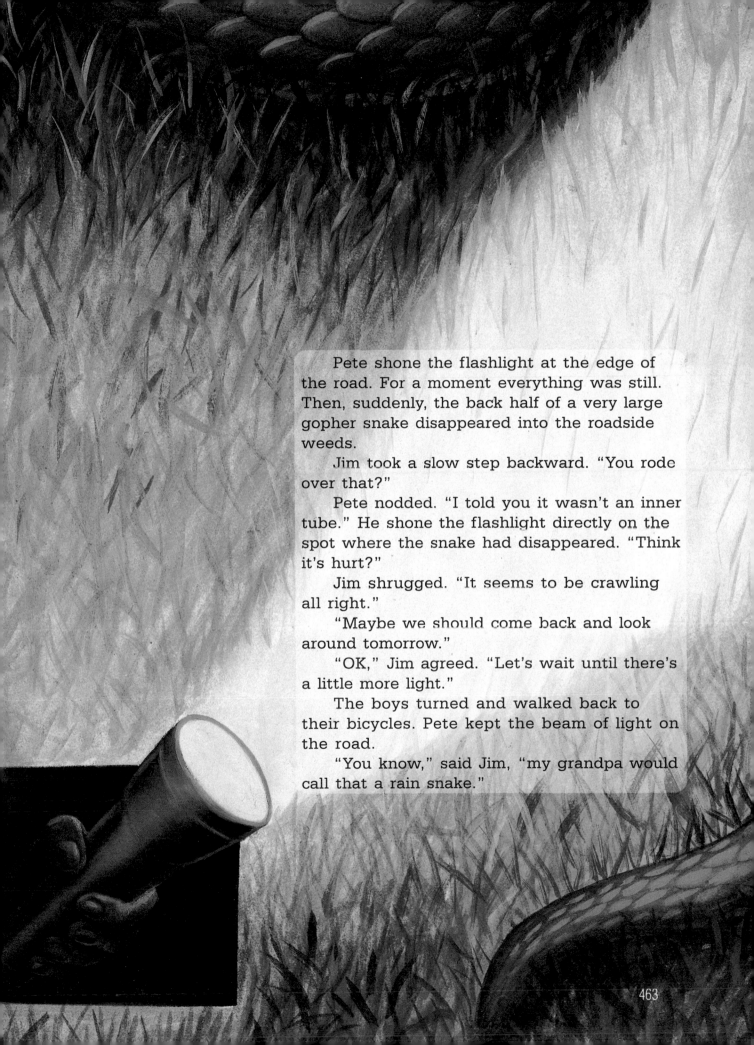

Pete shone the flashlight at the edge of the road. For a moment everything was still. Then, suddenly, the back half of a very large gopher snake disappeared into the roadside weeds.

Jim took a slow step backward. "You rode over that?"

Pete nodded. "I told you it wasn't an inner tube." He shone the flashlight directly on the spot where the snake had disappeared. "Think it's hurt?"

Jim shrugged. "It seems to be crawling all right."

"Maybe we should come back and look around tomorrow."

"OK," Jim agreed. "Let's wait until there's a little more light."

The boys turned and walked back to their bicycles. Pete kept the beam of light on the road.

"You know," said Jim, "my grandpa would call that a rain snake."

"What?" asked Pete.

"A rain snake. He'd say you could make it rain for sure with a snake like that."

"How?"

"Well," said Jim, "my grandpa grew up way back in the hills. When he was a boy, the farmers would sometimes use a dead snake to make it rain. They'd find a large tree with a strong low branch and throw the snake over the branch. A big snake like that would bring rain for sure."

Pete leaned over and picked up his bike. "You believe that?"

"Naw," answered Jim quickly. Then he scratched his head and looked back down the road. "But, well, I never tried it. I don't know. My grandpa says they did it a lot. Maybe it'd work for some people, sometimes. . . ."

What do you think? Can throwing a dead snake over a tree branch bring rain?

Every day you answer questions—dozens or even hundreds of them. What should I wear today? What assignments do I need for school? Can I eat an extra piece of toast and still get to the bus on time? What should I do tonight?

Some questions you answer correctly. Others you don't. Some questions are important. You spend lots of time thinking about them. Other questions aren't important. You guess at the answer or just choose an answer automatically.

How Do You Answer Questions?

You think about many things when you try to answer a question. You try to remember things you know that might help you. You look for new information about the question. Sometimes you try to guess how someone else would answer the question. Other times you might pick an answer because of what you would *like* the answer to be.

Sometimes these things help you find a correct answer. Other times they lead you to a wrong answer.

Here are three stories. Each story has a question. Each story tells about something that could happen to you, and each story will show a different way of answering a question.

INFORMATION

You're sitting on your bed one afternoon reading a book about a mountain climber. Things are getting very exciting (an avalanche has just started) when your little brother Ralphie walks into the room. He strolls past your bed and looks out the window.

"Hey," he says, "someone's in Mr. Murphy's backyard."

Your teeth start to grind. You've lost your place but you try not to show it. A long time ago you learned that sometimes the best way to get along with Ralphie is to ignore him.

"Hey," says Ralphie, "they're going into the Murphys' house."

You frown and roll over, wondering when Ralphie is going to go away.

"Hey," says Ralphie, "they're coming out of the Murphys' house. They're carrying something that's all covered up. They're stealing something from the Murphys!"

You sit up straight. The Murphys? Someone is stealing something from the Murphys?

AVALANCHE!

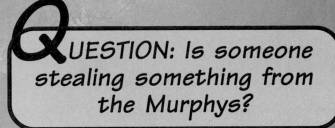

Then, out the window you see a truck. It is parked in front of the Murphys' house. Painted in large blue letters on the side of the truck are the words "Jake's TV Repair."

You shake your head.

"Go on," you tell Ralphie. "Take off."

"They're stealing something from the Murphys' house," says Ralphie. "The bad man just went back inside."

"It's not a bad man," you explain. "Someone's just picking up the TV. Can't you see that truck out there?"

"They're not taking the TV," Ralphie insists.

"Get out!" you shout.

"No!" says Ralphie.

"I said get out!" you scream, throwing a pillow at Ralphie.

So Ralphie finally leaves, walking out of the room very slowly.

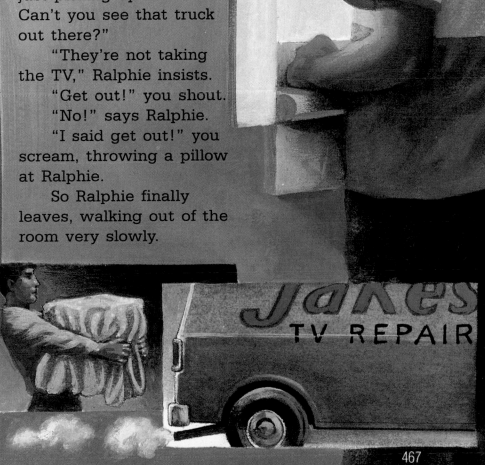

RRRING!

That night at dinner the telephone rings. Your father answers it. When he returns to the table, he says, "The Murphys just got home. While they were gone this afternoon, someone broke into their house and stole some money. The burglars also took some silverware and Mr. Murphy's violin.

"Most of our neighbors were gone this afternoon. The Johnsons didn't see anything because they were watching a repairman fix their TV all afternoon. Did any of you see anything?"

Ralphie sits up straight and begins nodding.

What happened? The question was: Is someone stealing something from the Murphys? You and Ralphie both made observations. Ralphie's observations told him the answer was yes. Your observations told you the answer was no. Why did you and Ralphie end up with different answers to the same question?

You answered the question incorrectly because of the way you used an observation. You saw a TV repair truck through the front window. Your observation was a good one. You noticed what kind of truck was on your street and where it was parked. The problem was how you used your observation. You thought the truck was giving you information about who was in the Murphys' house. Actually, Ralphie was giving you better information.

Information must be used carefully. Having information does not always mean you will answer a question correctly. If the information is not true or is not used in the right way, it can lead to a wrong answer.

It's Wednesday morning, just before lunch. Your teacher arranged for someone from the zoo to come and show your class some animals. You have seen an iguana, a mongoose, and a large snake. Now the zookeeper reaches into a wooden box and pulls out a fishbowl. He sets the bowl on a low table at the front of the room. Three small gray fish swim back and forth.

"Who knows the name of these fish?" asks the zookeeper.

Everyone is quiet. You stare at the fish for a moment. Of course you know what they are. They're guppies! They look just like the fish in your sister's aquarium. You've spent hours watching guppies.

Quickly, you raise your hand, but you're sitting in the last row and the zookeeper doesn't see you.

You wave your hand back and forth. The girl next to you ducks.

"These are gastromorphs," says the zookeeper. "They live in slow, muddy streams in Africa. They are very dangerous. They will eat almost anything that moves."

Quickly, you pull your hand down and look around. "Whew," you think. "That could have been embarrassing." Then you lean forward and squint at those fish again.

"We always keep a strong screen over this fishbowl when we visit schools. If anyone were to stick a hand in the water, well, these little fish would immediately attack and begin taking bites out of it."

GASTRO

This time the question seems easy. The fish look a lot like guppies. They swim like guppies. They're even the size and color of guppies. But would you stick your hand in the bowl? Of course not! The zookeeper just told you they are gastromorphs. Zookeepers know their animals, right? So the fish must be gastromorphs. Maybe.

Here's what really happened. The zookeeper who was supposed to visit your class got sick. The zoo sent over the person who normally takes care of birds. The zookeeper who came to your class knew a lot about birds, but not much about fish.

His first stop that morning was at the mammal house to pick up the mongoose. Then he went to the reptile house to get the iguana and the snake. He took all three animals with him into the fish house.

It was dark in the fish house. All the fish were arranged alphabetically in separate aquariums. The guppies were in the aquarium next to the gastromorphs. The zookeeper picked up a net, walked over to the gastromorphs, and leaned over the aquarium to dip some out. Just then the snake began to crawl out of its bag, so the zookeeper reached down to push it back in. When he stood up straight again he had three fish in his net. He dumped them into the fishbowl and hurried to your school. What he didn't know was that he had accidentally dipped the net into the wrong tank. He had netted three guppies instead of three gastromorphs.

472

MORPHS?

You really were right! The fish were guppies, but you changed your mind because of what the zookeeper said.

Sometimes other people are wrong. Usually zookeepers know much more about animals than you do, but maybe not every time. If you answer questions by depending too much on other people's answers, you probably will make mistakes.

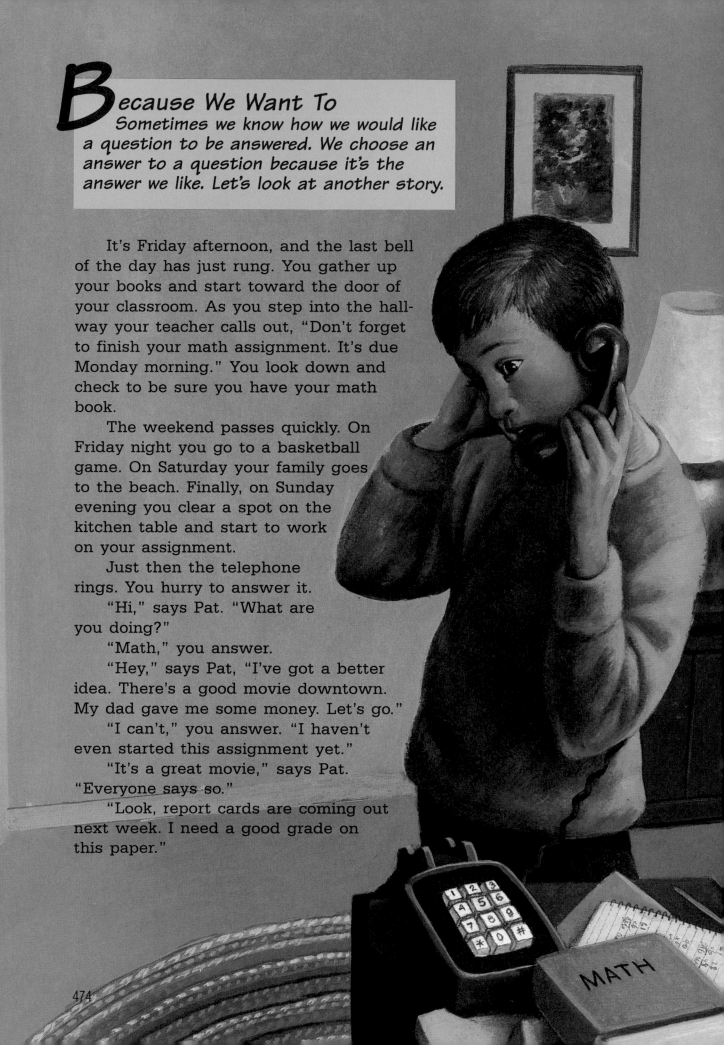

Because We Want To

Sometimes we know how we would like a question to be answered. We choose an answer to a question because it's the answer we like. Let's look at another story.

It's Friday afternoon, and the last bell of the day has just rung. You gather up your books and start toward the door of your classroom. As you step into the hallway your teacher calls out, "Don't forget to finish your math assignment. It's due Monday morning." You look down and check to be sure you have your math book.

The weekend passes quickly. On Friday night you go to a basketball game. On Saturday your family goes to the beach. Finally, on Sunday evening you clear a spot on the kitchen table and start to work on your assignment.

Just then the telephone rings. You hurry to answer it.

"Hi," says Pat. "What are you doing?"

"Math," you answer.

"Hey," says Pat, "I've got a better idea. There's a good movie downtown. My dad gave me some money. Let's go."

"I can't," you answer. "I haven't even started this assignment yet."

"It's a great movie," says Pat. "Everyone says so."

"Look, report cards are coming out next week. I need a good grade on this paper."

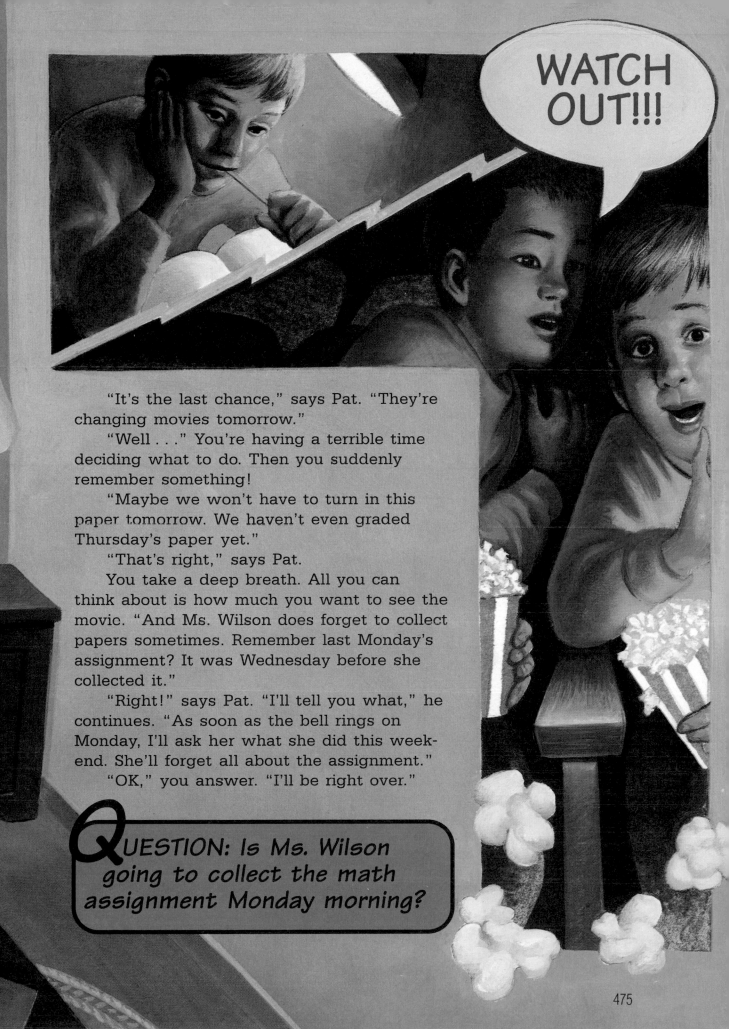

WATCH OUT!!!

"It's the last chance," says Pat. "They're changing movies tomorrow."

"Well . . ." You're having a terrible time deciding what to do. Then you suddenly remember something!

"Maybe we won't have to turn in this paper tomorrow. We haven't even graded Thursday's paper yet."

"That's right," says Pat.

You take a deep breath. All you can think about is how much you want to see the movie. "And Ms. Wilson does forget to collect papers sometimes. Remember last Monday's assignment? It was Wednesday before she collected it."

"Right!" says Pat. "I'll tell you what," he continues. "As soon as the bell rings on Monday, I'll ask her what she did this weekend. She'll forget all about the assignment."

"OK," you answer. "I'll be right over."

QUESTION: Is Ms. Wilson going to collect the math assignment Monday morning?

475

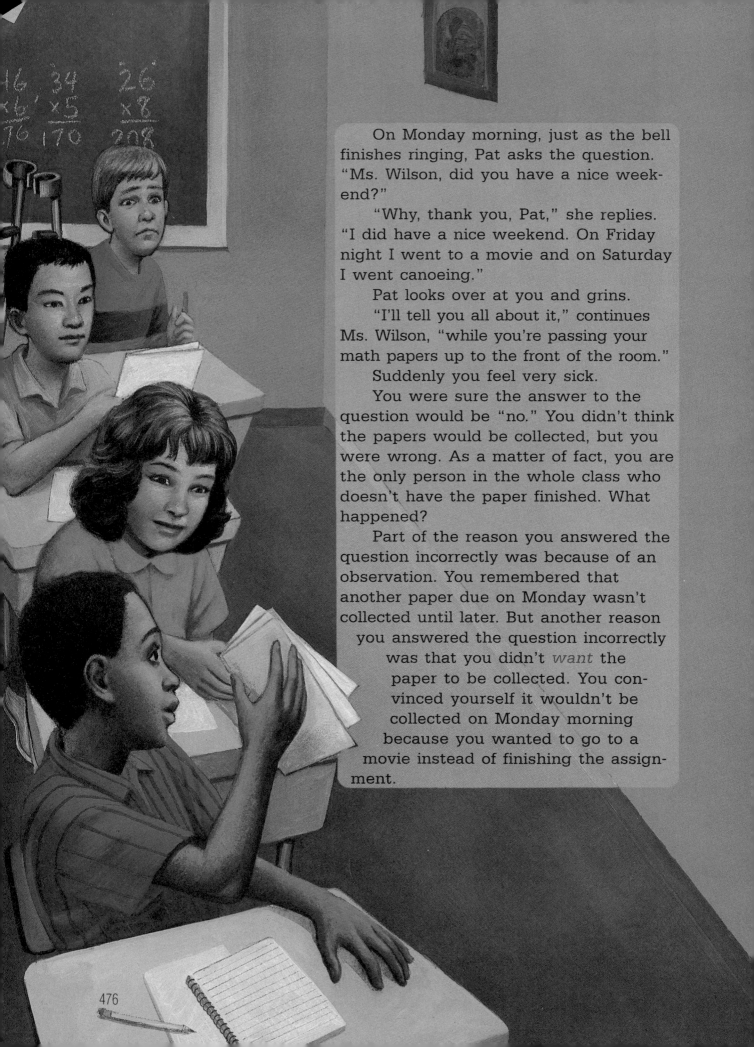

On Monday morning, just as the bell finishes ringing, Pat asks the question. "Ms. Wilson, did you have a nice weekend?"

"Why, thank you, Pat," she replies. "I did have a nice weekend. On Friday night I went to a movie and on Saturday I went canoeing."

Pat looks over at you and grins.

"I'll tell you all about it," continues Ms. Wilson, "while you're passing your math papers up to the front of the room."

Suddenly you feel very sick.

You were sure the answer to the question would be "no." You didn't think the papers would be collected, but you were wrong. As a matter of fact, you are the only person in the whole class who doesn't have the paper finished. What happened?

Part of the reason you answered the question incorrectly was because of an observation. You remembered that another paper due on Monday wasn't collected until later. But another reason you answered the question incorrectly was that you didn't *want* the paper to be collected. You convinced yourself it wouldn't be collected on Monday morning because you wanted to go to a movie instead of finishing the assignment.

Sometimes we really want the answer to a question to turn out in a certain way. Such a question can be difficult to answer correctly or fairly. Often it is easier to find an answer we like than an answer that is correct.

Carelessly used information, what others think, what we want to happen—none of these are very reliable ways of answering questions. Too many times they lead to wrong answers. Is there a better way? How can you find out whether throwing a dead snake over a tree branch really will bring rain?

There is a better way to find answers. Scientists use a series of steps called *the scientific method* to find accurate and reliable answers to their questions.

Good scientists are skeptical, but they keep an open mind. They know that experiments sometimes show that the correct answer to a question is not *always* the one you think it will be!

MEET STEPHEN P. KRAMER

Science has always fascinated Stephen P. Kramer. In college, he studied biology, the science of living things. After graduation, he taught science for four years on a Navajo reservation. Today, Kramer lives in Vancouver, Washington, where he writes and helps care for his two sons. His books combine his training as a biologist and his experience as a teacher. His first book, **Getting Oxygen: What Do You Do If You're Cell Twenty-Two?**, explains how the body gets and uses oxygen. **How to Think Like a Scientist** describes the scientific method, the step-by-step process that scientists use to learn about our world.

MY FLOOR IS SOMEBODY'S CEILING

My floor is somebody's ceiling
And my ceiling is somebody's floor.
So maybe my table is somebody's chair
And maybe my here is somebody's there,
And maybe my circle is somebody's square
And my window is somebody's door.
These are things I have wondered before,
But I think that I won't anymore.
No, I think that I won't anymore.

Jeff Moss

478

MEET
PATRICIA LAUBER

PATRICIA LAUBER WROTE HER FIRST BOOK AT THE URGING OF A FRIEND. LAUBER'S STORIES ABOUT CLARENCE, HER DOG, WERE SO ENTERTAINING THAT HER FRIEND URGED HER TO WRITE THEM DOWN. "CLARENCE AND I BOTH THOUGHT THIS WAS A FINE IDEA, . . ." SAYS LAUBER.

"THE RESULT WAS MY FIRST BOOK, **CLARENCE THE TV DOG.**" SINCE THEN, LAUBER HAS WRITTEN MORE THAN FIFTY BOOKS.

WRITING A NONFICTION BOOK REQUIRES "A GREAT DEAL OF RESEARCH," ACCORD- ING TO LAUBER. SHE READS, TALKS TO EXPERTS, AND VISITS KEY PLACES. FOR **THE NEWS ABOUT DINOSAURS**, SHE HAD TO MAKE SURE ALL THE ILLUSTRATIONS IN THE BOOK WERE SCIENTIFICALLY ACCURATE. MUCH OF THE ART LAUBER CHOSE WAS DONE BY PALEON- TOLOGISTS, SCIENTISTS WHO STUDY DINOSAURS.

FOR PATRICIA LAUBER, WRITING IS AN ACT OF SHARING. "WHEN I AM FULL OF ENTHUSIASM FOR A SUBJECT, I HAVE A STRONG DESIRE TO SHARE IT WITH OTHER PEOPLE."

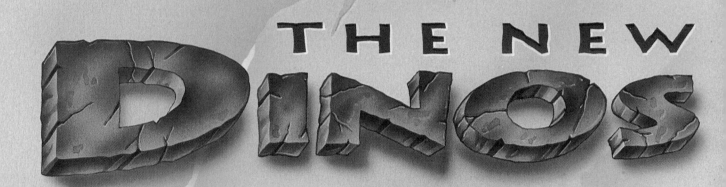

THE NEW DINOS

S ABOUT
AURS

BY PATRICIA LAUBER

Baryonyx was 30 feet long, with 15-inch claws and a snout like a crocodile's. It probably lived along rivers and used its claws and snout to catch fish. It was discovered near London, England, by a plumber whose hobby was searching for fossils, traces of ancient life preserved in rock. *Baryonyx* means "heavy claw." ▶

inosaurs were discovered in the early 1800s. Until then, no one had even guessed that once there were dinosaurs.

Scientists studied the big teeth and bones they had found. They wondered what kind of animals these belonged to. Finally they decided the animals were reptiles—relatives of today's crocodiles, turtles, snakes, and lizards. In 1841 the animals were named *dinosaurs,* meaning "terrible lizards."

Dinosaur hunters dug for bones. They found giant dinosaurs, dinosaurs the size of chickens, and many in-between sizes. They gave each kind a name. They fitted bones together and made skeletons. After a hundred or more years, this work seemed to be ending. Scientists began to think they had discovered nearly every kind of dinosaur that ever walked the earth.

The Natural History Museum, London

Baryonyx Walkeri

J.Wilbmes-996-

THE NEWS IS:

The work was far from finished. Today new kinds of dinosaurs are found all the time. And scientists think there must be hundreds more that they haven't discovered yet. Four of the new kinds they have found are *Baryonyx*, *Mamenchisaurus*, *Deinonychus*, and *Nanotyrannus*.

▲ *Mamenchisaurus* was a giant plant-eating dinosaur, 72 feet long. Its 33-foot neck is the longest of any known animal. The dinosaur is named for the place in China where it was found.

▲ *Nanotyrannus* was a pygmy tyrannosaur, a small relative of *Tyrannosaurus rex*. Its name means "pygmy tyrant." This small meat-eating dinosaur looked like its big relative but was only one-tenth as heavy and one-third as long—it weighed about 1,000 pounds and was 17 feet long. *Nanotyrannus* was discovered in a museum, where it had earlier been mistaken for another meat-eater, a gorgosaur, also known as *Albertosaurus*. Here its jaws are about to close on a smaller dinosaur.

486

Deinonychus was found in Montana. It was fairly small, about 9 feet long, and walked on its hind legs. Each hind foot had a big claw, shaped like a curved sword. The dinosaur's name means "terrible claw." Like other meat-eaters, *Deinonychus* spent much of its time resting or sleeping and digesting its last meal. This pair has just awakened, hungry and ready to hunt. ▼

M ost reptiles walk with their knees bent and their feet wide apart. Scientists used to think dinosaurs must have walked the same way. They pictured dinosaurs as slow and clumsy, waddling along with their tails dragging on the ground. So that was how dinosaurs were made to look in books and museums.

▲ For many years, people thought of dinosaurs as slow-moving and slow-witted. That is how they appear in this 1870s painting by Benjamin Waterhouse Hawkins. He was the first artist to work closely with scientists who were studying dinosaurs.

THE NEWS IS:

Dinosaurs didn't look like that at all. They were good walkers. They held their tails up. And many kinds were quick and nimble. Today's scientists have learned this by studying dinosaur footprints.

When dinosaurs walked in mud or wet sand, they left footprints. Most of these tracks washed or oozed away. But in some places the tracks hardened. Later they were buried under mud or sand that turned to rock. The tracks were preserved in the rock—they became fossils.

Today dinosaurs are shown as lively and active. These huge, horned plant-eaters are driving off *Albertosaurus*, a fierce meat-eater. ▼

By Gregory S. Paul © Gregory S. Paul 1988

Tracks show that dinosaurs walked in long, easy strides. Their legs and feet were under their bodies, not out to the side. Their bodies were high off the ground. Big plant-eaters walked at 3 or 4 miles an hour. Some small meat-eaters could run as fast as 35 or 40 miles an hour.

◀ At least some dinosaurs could swim. *Apatosaurus* has tried to escape a pack of *Allosaurus* by taking to the water— but the meat-eaters can swim, too.

◀ *Camarasaurs* (foreground) and *camptosaurs* are crossing a recently flooded area and leaving footprints. Preserved in rock, such tracks have revealed much about dinosaurs.

The biggest dinosaurs belonged to the group of plant-eaters named sauropods. Among them were *Mamenchisaurus*, *Diplodocus*, *Brachiosaurus*, *Apatosaurus*, and *Camarasaurus*. They were the longest, tallest, heaviest land animals that ever lived. They had legs like tree trunks, long tails, and long necks that ended in small heads.

Earlier scientists thought these giants spent their lives in shallow lakes or swamps, where water helped support their heavy bodies. Some scientists wondered if sauropods were able to walk on land at all.

Sauropods were very much at home on dry land. They may have spent some of their time in water, but they didn't live there. Their bones and footprints have been found in places that were dry part of the year and rainy part of the year. They have been found in places where forests of evergreens grew in the days of dinosaurs.

Footprints show that sauropods walked in long strides on all four feet. They may have reared up on their hind legs, using their tails for balance, to feed from the tops of trees.

Giant animals need giant amounts of food. A large sauropod must have eaten several hundred pounds of plant food a day. Perhaps sauropods traveled about, following the greening of forests as rainy seasons came and went.

▲ Sauropods were at home on dry land, where they used their long necks to reach into treetops for food. Shown here are *Camarasaurus* (left), *Barosaurus* (center), and *Apatosaurus* (right).

Like all sauropods, *Brachiosaurus* (left) and *Barosaurus* (right) moved easily on land, which was helpful when they met meat-eaters such as *Ceratosaurus* (center). ▼

▲ Sauropods probably traveled long distances to new sources of food.

Early dinosaur hunters discovered that many kinds and sizes of dinosaurs once roamed the earth.

Today's dinosaur hunters are discovering how dinosaurs lived—how they moved and traveled and fed and defended themselves. They are learning what dinosaurs were like before they hatched. They are even learning about dinosaur senses and voices.

The part of a skull that holds the brain is called a braincase. It shows the size and shape of the brain. It shows which parts of the brain were highly developed. In dinosaurs these parts were ones that receive information from the senses. Dinosaurs had good eyesight and a keen sense of smell. They also had a keen sense of hearing.

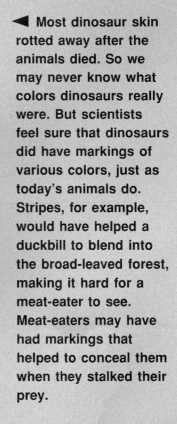

◄ Most dinosaur skin rotted away after the animals died. So we may never know what colors dinosaurs really were. But scientists feel sure that dinosaurs did have markings of various colors, just as today's animals do. Stripes, for example, would have helped a duckbill to blend into the broad-leaved forest, making it hard for a meat-eater to see. Meat-eaters may have had markings that helped to conceal them when they stalked their prey.

◄ Dinosaurs were alert. Their keen senses helped meat-eaters to find prey and plant-eaters to learn of danger.

497

A splash of color would call attention to the spiny neck frill of this horned dinosaur, which may have frightened meat-eaters. ▶

498

Still other bones show that dinosaurs had voices. Young dinosaurs may have squeaked and squealed. Bigger dinosaurs may have croaked, tootled, barked, bellowed, bayed, or made sounds like a tuba.

With all the new discoveries, perhaps it seems there's not much left to learn about dinosaurs.

Scientists will be finding new dinosaurs and learning about dinosaur lives for years to come. And when they do, their discoveries will be reported in the news.

By Mark Hallett © Mark Hallett 1985

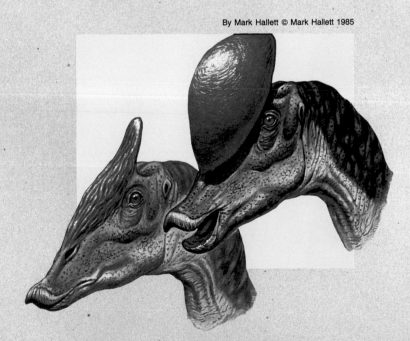

▲ Some dinosaurs may have had hollow pouches on their heads, which could be blown up and used to scare off enemies or to attract mates.

Fossils

Older than
books,
than scrolls,

older
than the first
tales told

or the
first words
spoken

are the stories

in forests that
turned to
stone

in ice walls
that trapped the
mammoth

in the long
bones of
dinosaurs—

the fossil
stories that begin
Once upon a time

Lilian Moore

What's The Story?

**From the Mixed-Up Files of
Mrs. Basil E. Frankweiler**
by E.L. Konigsburg
Aladdin, 1987

**101 Questions and Answers
about Dangerous Animals**
by Seymour Simon
illustrated by E. Friedman
Macmillan, 1985

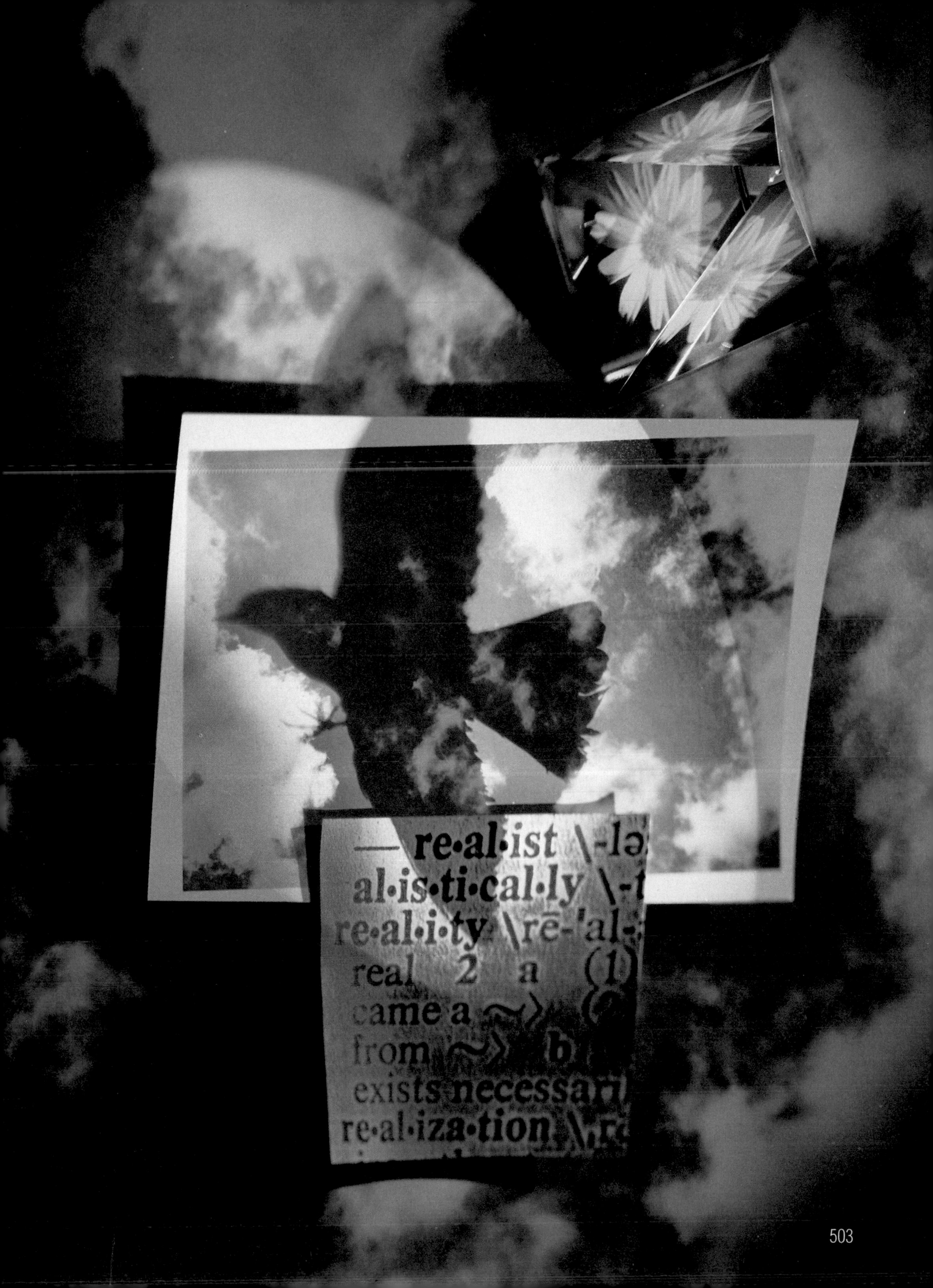

—re·al·ist \-lə
al·is·ti·cal·ly \-t
re·al·i·ty \rē-'al-
real 2 a (1
came a ~ >
from ~ > b
exists necessar
re·al·iza·tion \re

EINSTEIN

Meet Seymour Simon

Since 1968, Seymour Simon has been writing children's books on science topics ranging from paper airplanes to optical illusions. More than forty of these books have been named Outstanding Science Trade Books for Children. But it wasn't until 1980 that he began writing his Einstein Anderson fiction series. In these books, Simon combines mystery, science, and "bad puns." "The reader gets a chance to solve the puzzle," Simon points out, "and, I hope, gets a chance to learn something about science as well."

A former science teacher, Simon still finds joy in helping students learn. He loves to hear from readers who have tried an experiment in one of his books. Sharing a reader's discovery, he says, is "as much fun as the first time I found something out for myself."

504

ANDERSON

two stories by Seymour Simon
illustrations by Mary Thelen

THE INCREDIBLE SHRINKING MACHINE

THE IMPOS

Margaret Michaels was Einstein's good friend and arch rival. Science was their favorite subject. Einstein and Margaret were always talking about important things like atoms, planets, and who was the best science student.

Margaret's mother didn't quite know what to make of her daughter. Mrs. Michaels had wanted Margaret to take ballet classes on Saturday mornings. Margaret had insisted that she wanted to be in the Saturday Science Experimenters Club.

Mrs. Michaels thought that animals were nice when they were outside of her house. Margaret thought that animals were nice both outside and inside the house. She had a pet springer spaniel named Nova, two pet cats named Orville and Wilbur, a pet gerbil named Sammy, and assorted tropical fish. She hadn't named them yet.

SIBLE TRICK

"Children," Ms. Taylor said, "the school fair is scheduled for next Friday. There will be a used-book sale, a cookie and cake sale, and the usual kinds of booth activities, such as bobbing for apples. All the money earned from the fair will be used to help pay expenses for our school's long weekend at Big Lake State Park later this month."

Mrs. Michaels liked to listen to classical music. Margaret liked to listen to jazz. Mrs. Michaels was a member of the Sparta Choral Singing Society. Margaret couldn't sing a note in tune. But despite all the differences between them, Mrs. Michaels was very proud of her daughter's doings and boasted about her whenever she had the chance.

Margaret had left to visit her aunt for a week as soon as school was let out for the summer. Einstein knew that Margaret was back and wondered why she hadn't called him. Finally he decided to call and find out.

"Hello, Margaret, what's happening? How is your aunt? How come you didn't call?"

Ms. Taylor paused as the class started to buzz. Everyone was looking forward to the fair and also to the weekend at Big Lake. Ms. Taylor, Einstein's sixth grade teacher, waited a few minutes and then called on the class to quiet down.

"I want to appoint a committee to decide on our class booth at this year's fair. Try to come up with something

"Einstein," Margaret said, "I was just about to call you. Aunt Bess drove me home two days ago and stayed to visit my parents. She's going to drive back tomorrow, and she said it would be O.K. if I invited a friend to her house for the weekend. She's a biology professor at State University and has all kinds of science stuff at her house that you might like to see. How would you like to go?"

different. The class that earns the most money with its booth will go up to Big Lake a day early. Now who would like to serve on the committee? Hands, please."

Many children raised their hands to volunteer. Ms. Taylor chose six children, including Pat Burns and his pal Herman. She chose neither Einstein nor Margaret.

Einstein was about to refuse because his family was going to the beach on Sunday, when Margaret continued.

"Also, I have a science puzzle to show you at Aunt Bess's that even the great Einstein Anderson can't solve."

Well, that changed everything. Einstein couldn't turn down a science challenge from Margaret, so he agreed to go. He spent the rest of the day playing

Later, during lunch recess, Margaret was talking to Einstein. "I wonder why Ms. Taylor didn't choose either of us for that committee," she said. "Does she really expect Pat the Brat or Herman to come up with an original idea?"

baseball with some classmates and wondering about the puzzle that Margaret had mentioned.

Einstein and Margaret were driven by Aunt Bess early in the morning on Saturday. They arrived at Remsen, a town near the State University, just after 8:00 A.M. Aunt Bess's house was in a sort of clearing surrounded by trees. Instead of first going inside, Margaret led Einstein behind the house and down a twisting path in the woods.

Hidden from the house at the end of the path was a small shack with a bright yellow door. The early-morning sun shone directly on the yellow door and made it look almost like gold.

"Well, it's only fair that everyone gets a chance," Einstein replied. "And maybe Ms. Taylor thinks that scientists can't come up with a contest that's fun."

"I guess that's so," Margaret said glumly. "You haven't even cracked one joke all day long. Maybe too much science makes you lose your sense of humor."

"Lose my sense of humor!" exclaimed Einstein. "Not very likely! I'm just like the scientist who invented spaghetti. I can use my noodle to come up with an idea for a booth that will be the hit of the fair."

"Look, noodle head," Margaret said sweetly, "talk is cheap. Let's see you come up with a *science* booth that is funny and attractive. The committee is supposed to report tomorrow on their idea for a booth. Why don't you come up with your own idea? If it's better than the committee's idea, I'm sure the class will go along with it."

Margaret unlocked the yellow door and motioned Einstein inside. Einstein noticed that the single room they entered had no other doors and only one small window. The only objects in the room were a large stone table and a small black box sitting on the table.

"Einstein, look over the stone table closely," Margaret said. "It was put together right in this room. You can see that it is too big to pass through the door or the window. You would have to break it into little pieces to get it out of the room."

"I accept your challenge," said Einstein. "Science *can* be fun. In the meantime, let's go and eat an astronaut's favorite meal. Launch."

The next day the committee was giving their ideas about a booth for their class. They had elected Pat the Brat chairman because he had

Little Box

Big taBle

volunteered for it. Pat said that he would make a good chairman. Besides, he pointed out, looking at his fist, he was also the strongest kid in the class. No one else on the committee was prepared to argue the point.

"Here's what we decided to do," Pat reported to the class. "We're going to have a fortune-telling booth. I'm going to dress up with a turban, and we'll get a crystal ball. Then we'll charge ten cents apiece to tell people's fortunes."

"But, Pat, what do you know about telling fortunes?" Ms. Taylor asked.

"I could make them up," said Pat. "Who's going to know the difference?"

"Sure," called out Einstein, "Pat could dress up like a lady and we could call him Miss Fortune."

Pat glared at Einstein. "O.K., wise guy," he said. "You got a better idea for a booth?"

"It just so happens I have," answered Einstein. "Suppose our class has The Booth of the Impossible Trick. You have to pay a dime to try it out, and if you can do the trick you win a dollar."

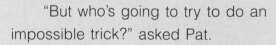

Einstein checked the table carefully. He could see that what Margaret said was true. You would need a bulldozer to break up that old stone table.

"I'm now going to switch on my incredible shrinking machine," said Margaret. She flipped a switch on the side of the little black box. Nothing much happened except that the black box sort of burped once and then was quiet.

"But who's going to try to do an impossible trick?" asked Pat.

"That's the good part," said Einstein. "The trick sounds like it's easy to do, but it's really impossible. We should get lots of people who'll try to win."

"That's stupid," said Pat. "How can a trick sound easy if it's really impossible?"

"Do you want to try it?" asked Einstein.

"Do I have to pay you a dime to try?" Pat asked suspiciously.

"No, this is for free," said Einstein. "All you have to do is bend over and touch your toes without bending your knees."

"What!" said Pat. "That's easy. I'll bet you a dime I can do that."

"There's just one more thing, Pat," Einstein said. "You have to begin with your back and your feet touching a wall. Your feet have to remain against the wall as you bend."

"So what?" said Pat. "I'm strong. I can touch my toes anywhere."

"Sorry," said Einstein, "but it can't be done."

Margaret motioned Einstein to follow her out. "We'll have to leave the room so as not to shrink ourselves," she said. "But when we come back in a few hours, the table will be gone without a trace. The incredible shrinking machine will have reduced it down to the size of an atom."

tHe SWitCH

tHe BOX

Margaret led Einstein back to Aunt Bess's house. For the rest of the day Einstein and Margaret experimented with chemical indicators such as litmus and brom thymol blue. They used a microscope to look at the protozoa in a drop of pond water. They fed food pellets to Aunt Bess's laboratory white mice. Lunch for Einstein and Margaret was peanut butter and jelly sandwiches.

Aunt Bess started an outdoor barbecue going late in the afternoon. They had grilled hamburgers, newly picked corn, a fresh tomato salad, and watermelon for dessert. It was all delicious and they didn't finish washing and straightening up till eight o'clock.

Can you solve the puzzle: *How does Einstein know that Pat cannot touch his toes without bending his knees when his feet are against a wall?*

Pat stood up against the front wall of the classroom and laughed. "Can you imagine?" he said. "Einstein is telling me that I can't touch my toes. Maybe he thinks I'm as weak as he is."

Pat started to bend over, but he quickly lost his balance. "Let me try that again," he said. Again Pat bent over and nearly fell down. He tried to do it several more times and then said in disgust, "That's impossible. No one can do it."

"That's just what I told you, Pat," said Einstein. "The trick sounds easy, but it's really impossible."

"Einstein, that's really a great idea," Ms. Taylor said. "I think it will make a terrific booth at the fair. Everyone

It was twilight when Margaret led Einstein back by a different path to the shack. They arrived just as the setting sun shone directly on the yellow door, turning it golden, just as it had done in the morning.

Margaret unlocked the door and they went inside. The room looked almost the same: one door, one small window, and one small black box. But the big stone table was gone. Nothing, not even a chip of stone, remained on the floor.

At first Einstein couldn't believe his eyes. Margaret might really stump him this time. How could that big stone table just disappear? Had Margaret really invented a shrinking machine?

Margaret smiled at the look on Einstein's face. "Well," she asked, "what do you think of my incredible shrinking machine?"

Einstein was quiet for a few minutes. Then his face changed and he began to laugh. He pushed back his glasses, which had slipped down. "You almost had me there for a minute, Margaret," he said. "I think I know what happened to the table. And if I'm correct, there is no such thing as an incredible shrinking machine."

will want to try it out. We can put the tryout place behind a curtain so that no one can see it's impossible to do."

Margaret raised her hand. "I agree with you, Ms. Taylor," she said. "It really is a great idea. Science *can*

be fun. But why is the trick impossible? Can you explain it to us?"

"Certainly, Margaret," replied Ms. Taylor. "The trick is impossible because . . . er . . . Would you please explain the trick, Einstein?"

Can you solve the puzzle: *What do you think happened to the table?*

"The key to the puzzle," Einstein began his explanation, "is the sun."

"The sun!" Margaret exclaimed. "What does the sun have to do with the shrinking machine?"

"You know that the sun rises in the east in the morning and sets in the west in the evening," Einstein explained. "Yet both the rising sun and the setting sun shone directly on the yellow door. That's impossible."

"So what's the answer?" Margaret asked.

"Sure," said Einstein. "It's all a matter of your center of gravity. That's the point where all your weight is concentrated. If your center of gravity is directly over your feet, then you're O.K. But if your center of gravity moves to a point outside your feet, then you fall over."

"But then how can you touch your toes at other times?" asked Ms. Taylor.

"Well, when you bend over freely, you shift your upper body weight forward and move your lower body weight backwards at the same time. That keeps your center of gravity from moving outside your feet. But with a wall at your back, you can't shift your

"Simple," Einstein said. "There must be two doors and two rooms in the shack, one in back and one in front. The sun shone on one door in the morning and on the other door in the afternoon. You must have taken me into one room in the morning but into the other room in the afternoon. The first room contained the stone table. The other room didn't have anything in it."

"You're right," said Margaret.

They left the shack and started back to the house. "I see that I made one mistake," Margaret said, shaking her head.

"What's that?" Einstein asked.

"I should have shown you my incredible shrinking machine on a cloudy day."

"Right," said Einstein. "Your machine had me in the dark for a while. But it was the sun that let me see the light."

lower body weight backwards. All your weight moves forward. So you fall over when you try to touch your toes."

"That's wonderful, Einstein," Margaret said to him later. "I'm sorry I called you a noodle head yesterday."

"It did me some good," said Einstein. "As Frankenstein said when he was hit by a bolt of lightning, 'Thanks, I needed that.'"

"You certainly haven't lost your sense of humor," Margaret said. "Unfortunately!"

BE A MATH SLEUTH

Science sleuth Einstein Anderson always uses his noodle to solve tricky problems. Now it's your turn! Use your noodle to solve these math puzzles. In a few cases, you'll need some paper and a pencil, too.

A *palindrome* is a word that is spelled the same backward and forward. *Noon* is a palindrome. So is *aha!* Numbers can be palindromes, too. The most recent palindromic year was 1991. What are the next *two* palindromic years?

LOOK BOTH WAYS

clue in the clock

Copy this clock face onto a sheet of paper. Then draw a line dividing your clock face in half so that the sum of the numbers in each half is the same. (The sum is part of the title of a famous Alfred Hitchcock movie mystery.)

Use the keypad on this telephone to decode this message. Because each number can stand for three different letters, this may be a trying experience.

4 2! 4 2! 8 3 7 9 "7 4 6 6 3 9!"

BREAK THE CODE!

Magic Mystery SQUARE

The sum of every row, column, and diagonal in a magic square is the same number. Copy this magic square onto a sheet of paper. Then fill in numbers to complete it. You can only use each number (one to nine) once.

2	7	6
	3	

THE FAMILY FORTUNE

Imagine that Lord and Lady Riches died under suspicious circumstances, leaving their large fortune to their children. There are nine sons. Each son has one sister. How many suspects, er, children are there altogether?

A "PET-ICULAR" PROBLEM

Imagine that Encyclopedia Brown, supersleuth, had two pets. His dog was three times as old as his cat. Two years later, though, the dog was only *twice* as old as his cat. How old were Encyclopedia's pets in each case?

Mastermind a math puzzle of your own. See if your friends can solve your puzzle.

521

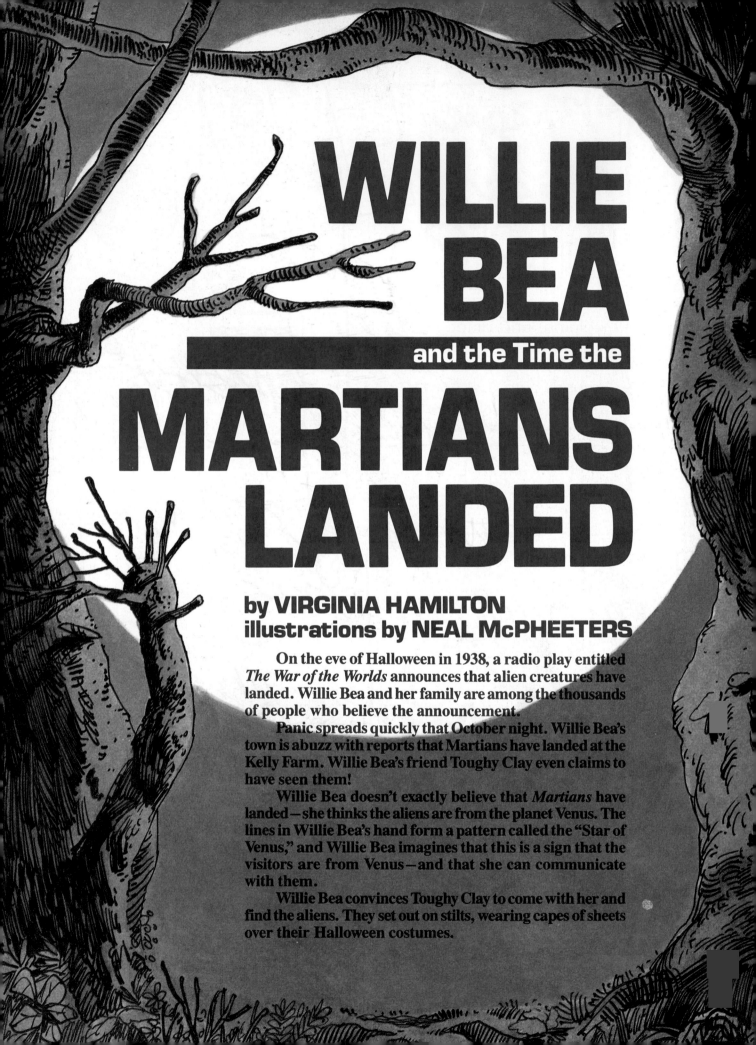

WILLIE BEA
and the Time the
MARTIANS LANDED

by VIRGINIA HAMILTON
illustrations by NEAL McPHEETERS

On the eve of Halloween in 1938, a radio play entitled *The War of the Worlds* announces that alien creatures have landed. Willie Bea and her family are among the thousands of people who believe the announcement.

Panic spreads quickly that October night. Willie Bea's town is abuzz with reports that Martians have landed at the Kelly Farm. Willie Bea's friend Toughy Clay even claims to have seen them!

Willie Bea doesn't exactly believe that *Martians* have landed—she thinks the aliens are from the planet Venus. The lines in Willie Bea's hand form a pattern called the "Star of Venus," and Willie Bea imagines that this is a sign that the visitors are from Venus—and that she can communicate with them.

Willie Bea convinces Toughy Clay to come with her and find the aliens. They set out on stilts, wearing capes of sheets over their Halloween costumes.

They strode the dark world, stilting. Willie Bea and Toughy Clay were out in the countryside. They were along roads, and through the fields whenever it was possible for them to get over fences.

The velveteen night and the distant, cold stars were what they could see traveling with them. They imagined they were alone on earth. Willie Bea could feel the loneliness in her heart and soul, and more than once she wished she was home.

Why'd I start this dumb, fool journey? she wondered.

They both imagined beings from another planet just out of sight in the dark.

Toughy Clay didn't dare turn around to check their backs, for fear he would see something beyond belief and fall. "You ever think what's gone happen if one of us fall off these dang stilts?" he whispered loudly to Willie Bea.

But she was thinking hard, and when she answered, it
was not about one of them falling. "The evening star of Venus
could be falling down on us this very minute," she told him.

"You think so?" he said anxiously.

"Sure," she said, "and maybe that Mars is falling down,
too. They say it is red and *mean,* boy!"

Wonder what is really going on, she thought. And if the
United States army can't stop them space men, what will
happen to *us?* And why come everything is so awful quiet
all around?

She felt strange, as if they were being watched. She was about to warn Toughy and tell him to shut off the flashlight. The light bobbed along with them. It was a weak light, batteries wearing out. It barely lit the side of the road. But it was what they had and a comfort in the dark.

Suddenly, there was a burst of flames close to a fence in a field they were passing. The flames grew rapidly into a huge bonfire. The fire flowed up and licked a pile of brush and brambles, crackling and sizzling hotly.

A gun went off with a roar. It was such a shock, all that fire and then the shot.

"Am I hit?" Toughy cried. He lost his grip on the flashlight, but he kept his balance. "Oh, lordy, somebody shootin' at us!"

Toughy had never been on the Kelly road before. But he recognized it from the years of stories he had heard about the farm.

"Are we that close? Keep your voice *down,*" she whispered.

"Look there," Toughy said. He stood, shifting back and forth to keep his balance.

Willie Bea shifted, too. But she was better at balancing than Toughy was. Just arm pressure and flexing leg muscles was all that was necessary. And once in a while moving the stilts an inch or two. "Look at what?" she said.

"There. Come over here," Toughy said.

She came up beside him. And what she saw made her feel like someone had shut down all her tiredness. Had turned off the cold of her hands and face. She didn't realize she was shivering, but the cold had got way under the hobo costume she had made.

They were on the private Kelly road and it had risen over a hillock. At first Willie Bea looked down at the reach of land.

"Is it the ice-skating lake?" she asked in the softest voice. Who could tell anything in this deep night?

"Uh-uh," Toughy said. "I hear the lake is on the other side of the house. Here is only the fields on each side of the private road."

"Well, I'm glad of that," Willie Bea said.

She thought to look up, gazing across and beyond the black land-reach to where there had to be some sort of hill. Over there, situated high and handsome, was the biggest house Willie Bea had ever seen. It was enormous. And it was lit up like a carnival, like a birthday cake.

"Havin' a Halloween ball?" she asked in awe.

She thought she heard strains of music coming from the mansion.

"Think they just own a lot of light," Toughy said. "Think they must be listenin' to their Victrola phonograph."

They don't even know the Venus ones are here! Willie Bea thought.

Another one came after the second. Two of them marching, rolling behind the first. They spread out to the left of the first one. Their blinding eyes outlined the first one. Illuminated it for Willie Bea to see plainly that it was a deadly, monstrous alien.

"It's true! It's an invasion!" Toughy was yelling. "Run. Run, Willie Bea!"

Willie Bea couldn't hear him. She couldn't move. She was transfixed by the monsters. The first one's neck wasn't in the center of its body, where it should have been. It was on the right *side* of it! The long neck was like a wide stovepipe jutting out of its side. Its head that fitted on its neck was *all* V-shaped.

Suddenly, it seemed that the first monster spoke to her. She was staring into its awful eye, into its noise. The darkness moving one by one was overpowering.

All went quiet inside Willie Bea. She no longer heard the monster's roaring noise. Its sound of voice was right with her,

The sun is an orange dinghy
　　　sailing across a calm sea.

It is a gold coin
　　　dropped down a drain in heaven.

It is a yellow beach ball
　　　kicked high into the summer sky.

It is a red thumb-print
　　　on a sheet of pale blue paper.

It is the gold top from a milk bottle
　　　floating on a puddle.

Wes Magee

WHAT IS...

Dramatic images of the sun often appear in Mexican art, as shown in these suns made of tinware, baked clay, and painted wood.

INFORMATION ILLUSTRATED

YOUR GUIDE TO A WORLD OF INFORMATION — WITH EXAMPLES
RELATED TO THE THEMES YOU HAVE BEEN READING ABOUT!

CONTENTS

Population of U.S. Cities

Source: U.S. Bureau of the Census (100 most populated cities ranked by July 1, 1988 estimates)

Rank	City	1988	1980	1970	1960	1950	1900	1850
1	New York, N.Y.	7,352,700	7,071,639	7,895,563	7,781,984	7,891,957	3,437,202	696,115
2	Los Angeles, Cal.	3,352,710	2,966,850	2,811,801	2,479,015	1,970,358	102,479	1,610
3	Chicago, Ill.	2,977,520	3,005,072	3,369,357	3,550,404	3,620,962	1,698,575	29,963
4	Houston, Tex.	1,698,090	1,595,138	1,233,535	938,219	596,163	44,633	2,396
5	Philadelphia, Pa.	1,647,000	1,688,210	1,949,996	2,002,512	2,071,605	1,293,697	121,376
6	San Diego, Cal.	1,070,310	875,538	697,471	573,224	334,387	17,700	...
7	Detroit, Mich.	1,035,920	1,203,339	1,514,063	1,670,144	1,849,568	285,704	21,019
8	Dallas, Tex.	987,360	904,078	844,401	679,684	434,462	42,638	...
9	San Antonio, Tex.	941,150	785,880	654,153	587,718	408,442	53,321	3,488
10	Phoenix, Ariz.	923,750	789,704	584,303	439,170	106,818	5,544	...
11	Baltimore, Md.	751,400	786,775	905,787	939,024	949,708	508,957	169,054
12	San Jose, Cal.	738,420	629,442	459,913	204,196	95,280	21,500	...
13	San Francisco, Ca.	731,600	678,974	715,674	740,316	775,357	342,782	34,776
14	Indianapolis, Ind.	727,130	700,807	736,856	476,258	427,173	169,164	8,091
15	Memphis, Tenn.	645,190	646,356	623,988	497,524	396,000	102,320	8,841
16	Jacksonville, Fla.	635,430	540,920	504,265	201,030	204,517	28,429	1,045
17	Washington, D.C.	617,000	638,333	756,668	763,956	802,178	278,718	40,001
18	Milwaukee, Wis.	599,380	636,212	717,372	741,324	637,392	285,315	20,061
19	Boston, Mass.	577,830	562,994	641,071	697,197	801,444	560,892	136,881
20	Columbus, Oh.	569,570	564,871	540,025	471,316	375,901	125,560	17,882
21	New Orleans, La.	531,700	557,515	593,471	627,525	570,445	287,104	116,375
22	Cleveland, Oh.	521,370	573,822	750,879	876,050	914,808	381,768	17,034
23	El Paso, Tex.	510,970	425,259	322,261	276,687	130,485	15,906	...
24	Seattle, Wash.	502,200	493,846	530,831	557,087	467,591	80,671	...
25	Denver, Col.	492,200	492,365	514,678	493,887	415,786	133,859	...
26	Nashville-Davidson, Tenn.	481,400	455,651	426,029	170,874	174,307	80,865	10,165
27	Austin, Tex.	464,690	345,496	253,539	186,545	132,459	22,258	629
28	Kansas City, Mo.	438,950	448,159	507,330	475,539	456,622	163,752	...
29	Oklahoma City, Okla.	434,380	403,213	368,164	324,253	243,504	10,037	...
30	Fort Worth, Tex.	426,610	385,164	393,455	356,268	278,778	26,688	...
31	Atlanta, Ga.	420,220	425,022	495,039	487,455	331,314	89,872	2,572
32	Portland, Ore.	418,470	366,383	379,967	372,676	373,628	90,426	...
33	Long Beach, Cal.	415,040	361,334	358,879	344,168	250,767	2,252	...
34	St. Louis, Mo.	403,700	453,085	622,236	750,026	856,796	575,238	77,860
35	Tucson, Ariz.	385,720	330,537	262,933	212,892	45,454	7,531	...
36	Albuquerque, N.M.	378,480	331,767	244,501	201,189	96,815	6,238	...
37	Honolulu, Ha.	376,110	762,874	630,528	294,194	248,034	39,306	...
38	Pittsburgh, Pa.	375,230	423,938	520,089	604,332	676,806	321,616	46,601
39	Miami, Fla.	371,100	346,865	334,859	291,688	249,276	1,681	...
40	Cincinnati, Oh.	370,480	385,457	453,514	502,550	503,998	325,902	115,435
41	Tulsa, Okla.	368,330	360,919	330,350	261,685	182,740	1,390	...
42	Charlotte, N.C.	367,860	314,447	241,420	201,564	134,042	18,091	1,065
43	Virginia Beach, Va.	365,300	262,199	172,106	8,091	5,390	...	...
44	Oakland, Cal.	356,860	339,337	361,561	367,548	384,575	66,960	...
45	Omaha, Neb.	353,170	314,255	346,929	301,598	251,117	102,555	...
46	Minneapolis, Minn.	344,670	370,951	434,400	482,872	521,718	202,718	...
47	Toledo, Oh.	340,760	354,635	383,062	318,003	303,616	131,822	3,829
48	Sacramento, Cal.	338,220	275,741	257,105	191,667	137,572	29,282	6,820
49	Newark, N.J.	313,800	329,248	381,930	405,220	438,776	246,070	38,894
50	Buffalo, N.Y.	313,570	357,870	462,768	532,759	580,132	352,387	42,261
51	Fresno, Cal.	307,090	218,202	165,655	133,929	91,669	12,470	...
52	Wichita, Kan.	295,320	279,272	276,554	254,698	168,279	24,671	...
53	Norfolk, Va.	286,500	266,979	307,951	304,869	213,513	46,624	14,326
54	Colorado Springs, Col.	283,110	215,150	135,517	70,194	45,472	21,085	...
55	Louisville, Ky.	281,880	298,451	361,706	390,639	369,129	204,731	43,194
56	Tampa, Fla.	281,790	271,523	277,714	274,970	124,681	15,839	...
57	Mesa, Ariz.	280,360	152,453	63,049	33,772	16,790	722	...
58	Birmingham, Ala.	277,280	284,413	300,910	340,887	326,037	38,415	...
59	Corpus Christi, Tex.	260,360	231,999	204,525	167,690	108,287	4,703	...
60	St. Paul, Minn.	259,110	270,230	309,866	313,411	311,349	163,065	1,112
61	Arlington, Tex.	257,460	160,113	90,229	44,775	7,692	1,079	...
62	Anaheim, Cal.	244,670	219,311	166,408	104,184	14,556	1,456	...
63	Santa Ana, Cal.	239,540	203,713	155,710	100,350	45,533	4,933	...
64	St. Petersburg, Fla.	235,450	238,647	216,159	181,298	96,738	1,575	...
65	Baton Rouge, La.	235,270	346,029	165,921	152,419	125,629	11,269	3,905
66	Rochester, N.Y.	229,780	241,741	295,011	318,611	332,488	162,608	36,403
67	Lexington-Fayette, Ky.	225,700	204,165	108,137	62,810	55,534	26,369	8,159
68	Akron, Oh.	221,510	237,177	275,425	290,351	274,605	42,728	3,266
69	Aurora, Col.	218,720	158,588	74,974	48,548	11,421	202	...
70	Anchorage, Alas.	218,500	174,431	48,081	44,237	11,254	...	...
71	Shreveport, La.	218,010	205,820	182,064	164,372	127,206	16,013	1,728

(continued)

Science & Technology — Gene Therapy; Inventions   191

she lacked. If the procedure is successful, the genetically engineered blood cells will pump out normal levels of the crucial enzyme and restore the girl's immune system to full health.

The specific disorder the girl suffers from is adenosine deaminase (ADA) deficiency, which results from a lack of the ADA gene, which makes an enzyme needed to clean up dangerous metabolic byproducts in the body.

The experimental procedure was developed by Dr. R. Michael Blaese of the National Cancer Institute, Dr. W. French Anderson of the National Heart, Lung and Blood Institute, and Dr. Kenneth W. Culver.

Inventions and Discoveries

Invention	Date	Inventor	Nation.
Adding machine	1642	Pascal	French
Adding machine	1885	Burroughs	US
Aerosol spray	1926	Rotheim	Norwegian
Air brake	1868	Westinghouse	US
Air conditioning	1911	Carrier	US
Air pump	1654	Guericke	German
Airplane, automatic pilot	1912	Sperry	US
Airplane, experimental	1896	Langley	US
Airplane jet engine	1939	Ohain	German
Airplane with motor	1903	Wright bros.	US
Airplane, hydro	1911	Curtiss	US
Airship	1852	Giffard	French
Airship, rigid dirigible	1900	Zeppelin	German
Arc welder	1919	Thomson	US
Autogyro	1920	de la Cierva	Spanish
Automobile, differential gear	1885	Benz	German
Automobile, electric	1892	Morrison	US
Automobile, exp'mtl	1864	Marcus	Austrian
Automobile, gasoline	1889	Daimler	German
Automobile, gasoline	1892	Duryea	US
Automobile magneto	1897	Bosch	German
Automobile muffler	...	Maxim, H.P.	US
Automobile self-starter	1911	Kettering	US
Babbitt metal	1839	Babbitt	US
Bakelite	1907	Baekeland	Belg US
Balloon	1783	Montgolier	French
Barometer	1643	Torricelli	Italian
Bicycle, modern	1885	Starley	English
Bifocal lens	1780	Franklin	US
Block signals, railway	1867	Hall	US
Bomb, depth	1916	Tait	US
Bottle machine	1895	Owens	US
Braille printing	1829	Braille	French
Burner, gas	1855	Bunsen	German
Calculating machine	1833	Babbage	English
Camera—see also Photography			
Camera, Kodak	1888	Eastman, Walker	US
Camera, Polaroid Land	1948	Land	US
Car coupler	1873	Janney	US
Carburetor, gasoline	1893	Maybach	German
Card time recorder	1894	Cooper	US
Carding machine	1797	Whittemore	US
Carpet sweeper	1876	Bissell	US
Cassette, audio	1963	Philips Co	Dutch
Cassette, videotape	1969	Sony	Japanese
Cash register	1879	Ritty	US
Cathode ray oscilloscope	1897	Braun	German
Cathode ray tube	1878	Crookes	English
CAT scan (computerized tomography)	1973	Hounsfield	English
Cellophane	1908	Brandenberger	Swiss
Celluloid	1870	Hyatt	US
Cement, Portland	1824	Aspdin	English

Invention	Date	Inventor	Nation.
Chronometer	1761	Harrison	English
Circuit, integrated	1959	Kilby, Noyce Texas Instr	US
Clock, pendulum	1657	Huygens	Dutch
Coaxial cable system	1929	Atlel, Espensched	US
Coke oven	1893	Hoffman	Austrian
Compressed air rock drill	1871	Ingersoll	US
Comptometer	1887	Feit	US
Computer, automatic sequence	1944	Aiken et al.	US
Computer, mini	1960	Digital Corp.	US
Condenser microphone (telephone)	1916	Wente	US
Contraceptive, oral	1954	Pincus, Rock	US
Corn, hybrid	1917	Jones	US
Cotton gin	1793	Whitney	US
Cream separator	1878	DeLaval	Swedish
Cultivator, disc	1878	Mallon	US
Cystoscope	1878	Nitze	German
Diesel engine	1895	Diesel	German
Disk, compact	1972	RCA	US
Disk, floppy	1970	IBM	US
Disk player, compact	1979	Sony, Philips Co.	Japanese, Dutch
Disk, video	1972	Philips Co.	Dutch
Dynamite	1866	Nobel	Swedish
Dynamo, continuous current	1871	Gramme	Belgian
Dynamo, hydrogen cooled	1915	Schuler	US
Electric battery	1800	Volta	Italian
Electric fan	1882	Wheeler	US
Electrocardiograph	1903	Einthoven	Dutch
Electroencephalograph	1929	Berger	German
Electromagnet	1824	Sturgeon	English
Electron spectrometer	1944	Deutsch, Elliott, Evans	US
Electron tube multigrid	1913	Langmuir	US
Electroplating	1805	Brugnatelli	Italian
Electrostatic generator	1929	Van de Graaff	US
Elevator brake	1852	Otis	US
Elevator, push button	1922	Larson	US
Engine, automatic transmission	1910	Fotinger	German
Engine, coal-gas 4-cycle	1876	Otto	German
Engine, compression ignition	1883	Daimler	German
Engine, electric ignition	1883	Benz	German
Engine, gas, compound	1926	Eickemeyer	US
Engine, gasoline	1872	Brayton, Geo	US
Engine, gasoline	1889	Daimler	German
Engine, steam, piston	1705	Newcomen	English
Engine, steam, piston	1769	Watt	Scottish
Engraving, half-tone	1852	Talbot	US

(continued)

ATLAS

Inset map (North America)
ARCTIC OCEAN
Alaska
NORTH
AMERICA
PACIFIC
OCEAN

Alaska Map

ARCTIC OCEAN

Chukchi Sea
Point Barrow
Beaufort Sea

70°N
170°W
160°W
150°W
140°W

Prudhoe Bay
Prudhoe Bay

130°W

70°N

Point Hope

BROOKS RANGE

Davidson Mountains

Arctic Circle

Arctic Circle

Bering Strait

Nome

CANADA

ST. LAWRENCE ISLAND

170°W

Yukon River

Kuskokwim Mountains

Fairbanks

60°N

ALASKA RANGE

Kuskokwim River

Anchorage
Valdez

ALASKA HIGHWAY

Bering Sea

Cook Inlet

60°N

Bristol Bay

Juneau

ALASKA PENINSULA

KODIAK ISLAND

GULF OF ALASKA

140°W

ALEXANDER ARCHIPELAGO

UNIMAK ISLAND

150°W

Ketchikan

Unimak Pass

160°W

PACIFIC OCEAN

130°W

ALASKA KEY

★ State capital
• Other city
▲ Mt. McKinley
 highest point in North America
 20,320 ft. (6,194 m)
⋯⋯ Continental Divide
── Trans–Alaska Pipeline
── Major road
▨ National park

0 50 100 150 Miles
0 50 100 150 Kilometers

Aleutian Islands Inset

180°
170°W
UNIMAK ISLAND

ATTU ISLAND

Bering Sea

ALEUTIAN ISLANDS

Unimak Pass

Amchitka Pass
Amukta Pass

0 50 100 150 Miles
0 50 100 150 Kilometers

50°N

PACIFIC OCEAN

180°
170°W

50°N

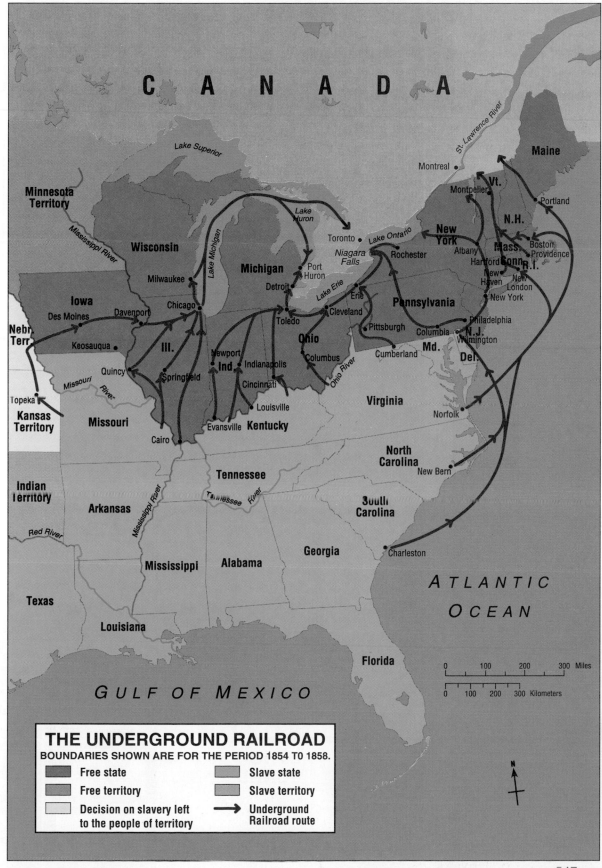

C A N A D A

Lake Superior

Minnesota
Territory

Wisconsin

Lake Huron

Montreal

Maine

Montpelier

Vt.

Portland

N.H.

Toronto

Lake Ontario

Niagara
Falls

Rochester

New
York

Albany

Mass.

Boston
Providence

R.I.

Hartford

Conn.

Milwaukee

Michigan

Port
Huron

Iowa

Des Moines

Davenport

Chicago

Detroit

Lake Erie

Erie

Cleveland

Pennsylvania

New
Haven

New
London

New York

Nebr.
Terr.

Keosauqua

Ill.

Pittsburgh

Columbia

Philadelphia

N.J.

Quincy

Newport

Ind.

Indianapolis

Ohio

Columbus

Cumberland

Wilmington

Del.

Md.

Springfield

Cincinnati

Topeka

Evansville

Louisville

Kansas
Territory

Cairo

Kentucky

Virginia

Norfolk

Missouri

North
Carolina

New Bern

Indian
Territory

Tennessee

Tennessee River

South
Carolina

Arkansas

Red River

Mississippi

Alabama

Georgia

Charleston

Texas

A T L A N T I C
O C E A N

Louisiana

Florida

G U L F   O F   M E X I C O

Mississippi River

Missouri River

St. Lawrence River

Lake Michigan

Ohio River

0   100   200   300 Miles

0   100   200   300 Kilometers

N

THE UNDERGROUND RAILROAD

BOUNDARIES SHOWN ARE FOR THE PERIOD 1854 TO 1858.

Free state

Slave state

Free territory

Slave territory

Decision on slavery left
to the people of territory

Underground
Railroad route

CARD CATALOG AND LIBRARY CLASSIFICATION SYSTEMS

CATALOG CARDS

J 971.91

KLONDIKE RIVER VALLEY (YUKON)--GOLD DISCOVERIES

Ray, Delia

 Gold! The Klondike adventure. New York: Lodestar Books © 1989. 90 pp. ; ill.

SUBJECT CARD

J 971.91

 Gold! The Klondike adventure.

 Ray, Delia

 Gold! The Klondike adventure. New York: Lodestar Books © 1989. 90 pp. ; ill.

TITLE CARD

J 971.91

 Ray, Delia

 Gold! The Klondike adventure. New York: Lodestar Books © 1989. 90 pp. ; ill.

 Includes glossary. An account of the Klondike gold rush.

 1. Klondike River Valley (Yukon)--Gold discoveries.

AUTHOR CARD

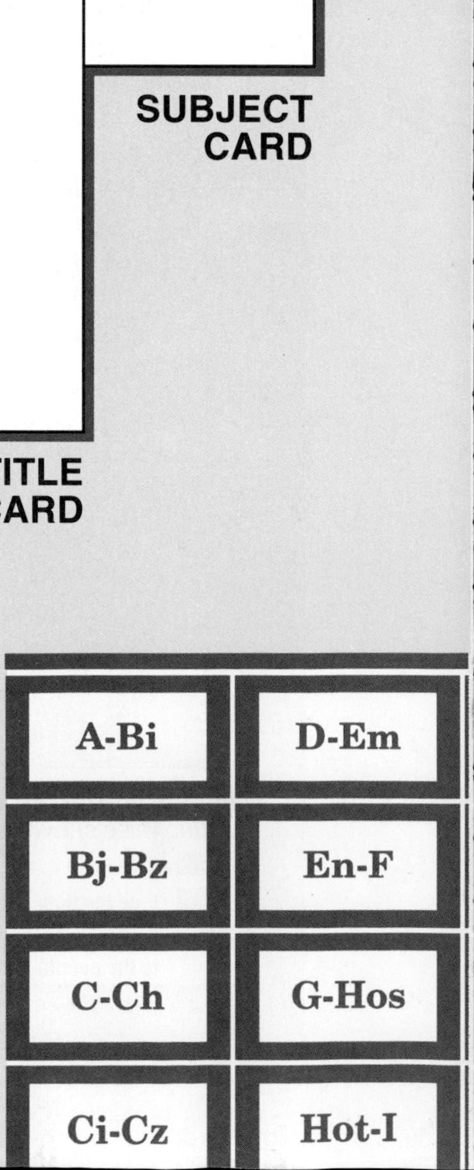

A-Bi	D-Em
Bj-Bz	En-F
C-Ch	G-Hos
Ci-Cz	Hot-I

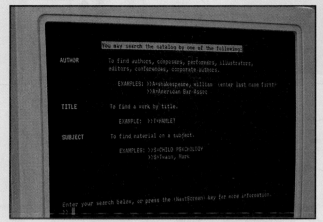

**COMPUTERIZED FORM
OF THE CARD CATALOG**

**BOOK FORM
OF THE CARD CATALOG**

LIBRARY CLASSIFICATION SYSTEMS

000–099	Generalities
100–199	Philosophy
200–299	Religion
300–399	Social Sciences
400–499	Language
500–599	Pure Sciences
600–699	Technology (Applied Sciences)
700–799	The Arts
800–899	Literature and Rhetoric
900–999	General Geography, History, and Related Disciplines

**DEWEY DECIMAL
CLASSIFICATION
SYSTEM (DDC)**

J-Ken	Pe-Q	Ta-Tim
Keo-L	R-Rom	Tin-V
M-Nos	Rom-Sm	Wa-Wis
Not-Pa	Sn-Sz	Wit-Z

A	General Works
B	Philosophy – Religion
C	History – Auxiliary Sciences
D	History and Topography (except America)
E-F	American History
G	Geography, Anthropology, Folklore, Manners and Customs, Recreation
H	Social Sciences
J	Political Sciences
K	Law of the United States
L	Education
M	Music and Books on Music
N	Fine Arts
P	Language and Literature
Q	Science
R	Medicine
S	Agriculture – Plant and Animal Industry
T	Technology
U	Military Science
V	Naval Science
W	Bibliography and Library Science

**LIBRARY OF CONGRESS
CLASSIFICATION SYSTEM (LC)**

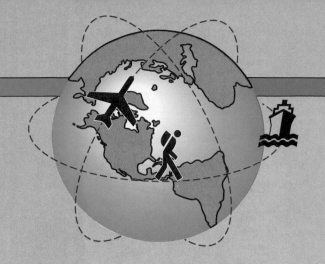

SOME NOTABLE TRIPS AROUND THE WORLD

PERSON(S)	BY	POINT OF DEPARTURE AND RETURN	TIME				YEAR(S)	REMARKS
			YEARS	DAYS	HOURS	MINUTES		
Crew of the *Vittoria*, Magellan Expedition	sea	Sanlúcar, Spain	2	351			1519–1522	first successful circumnavigation
Nellie Bly	land, sea	New York, N.Y.		72	6	11	1889	fastest trip to date
Joshua Slocum	sea	Newport, R.I.	3	70			1895–1898	first solo by sea
J.W. Willis Sayre	land, sea	Seattle, Wash.		54	9	42	1903	
Lowell H. Smith and Leslie P. Arnold Erik H. Nelson and John Harding	air	Seattle, Wash.		35	1	11	1924	first by air
Wiley Post and Harold Gatty	air	New York, N.Y.		8	15	51	1931	
Wiley Post	air	New York, N.Y.		4	19	36	1933	first solo by air
James Gallagher	air	Ft. Worth, Texas		3	22	1	1949	first nonstop by air*
Sue Snyder	air	Chicago, Ill.		2	14	59	1960	
Robin Knox Johnston	sea	Falmouth, England		312			1968–1969	first nonstop solo by sea
David Kunst	land	Waseca, Minn.	4	117			1970–1974	first by foot
Richard Rutan and Jeana Yeager	air	Edwards Air Force Base, Calif.		9	0	3	1986	first nonstop by air without refueling
Clay Lacey	air	Seattle, Wash.			36	54	1988	fastest by air to date
Tituoan Lamazou	sea	Les Sables, France		109	8	48	1989–1990	fastest nonstop by sea to date

* refueled in flight

ROAD MILEAGE BETWEEN SOME U. S. CITIES

	Atlanta, Ga.	Boston, Mass.	Chicago, Ill.	Cleveland, Ohio	Dallas, Texas	Denver, Colo.	Detroit, Mich.	Kansas City, Mo.	Los Angeles, Calif.	Memphis, Tenn.	Minneapolis, Minn.	New Orleans, La.	New York, N.Y.	Omaha, Nebr.	Pittsburgh, Pa.	Portland, Ore.	San Francisco, Calif.	Seattle, Wash.	Tulsa, Okla.	Washington, D.C.
Atlanta, Ga.		1,037	674	672	795	1,398	699	798	2,182	371	1,068	479	841	986	687	2,601	2,496	2,618	772	608
Boston, Mass.	1,037		963	628	1,748	1,949	695	1,391	2,979	1,296	1,368	1,507	206	1,412	561	3,046	3,095	2,976	1,537	429
Chicago, Ill.	674	963		335	917	996	266	499	2,054	530	405	912	802	459	452	2,083	2,142	2,013	683	671
Cleveland, Ohio	672	628	335		1,159	1,321	170	779	2,367	712	740	1,030	473	784	129	2,418	2,467	2,348	925	346
Dallas, Texas	795	1,748	917	1,159		781	1,143	489	1,387	452	936	496	1,552	644	1,208	2,009	1,753	2,078	257	1,319
Denver, Colo.	1,398	1,949	996	1,321	781		1,253	600	1,059	1,040	841	1,273	1,771	537	1,411	1,238	1,235	1,307	681	1,616
Detroit, Mich.	699	695	266	170	1,143	1,253		743	2,311	713	671	1,045	637	716	287	2,349	2,399	2,279	909	506
Kansas City, Mo.	798	1,391	499	779	489	600	743		1,589	482	443	806	1,198	201	838	1,809	1,861	1,858	248	1,042
Los Angeles, Calif.	2,182	2,979	2,054	2,367	1,387	1,059	2,311	1,589		1,817	1,889	1,883	2,786	1,595	2,426	959	379	1,131	1,452	2,631
Memphis, Tenn.	371	1,296	530	712	452	1,040	713	482	1,817		826	390	1,100	652	752	2,259	2,125	2,290	401	867
Minneapolis, Minn.	1,068	1,368	405	740	936	841	671	443	1,889	826		1,214	1,207	357	857	1,678	1,940	1,608	695	1,090
New Orleans, La.	479	1,507	912	1,030	496	1,273	1,045	806	1,883	390	1,214		1,311	1,007	1,070	2,505	2,249	2,574	647	1,078
New York, N.Y.	841	206	802	473	1,552	1,771	637	1,198	2,786	1,100	1,207	1,311		1,251	368	2,885	2,934	2,815	1,344	233
Omaha, Nebr.	986	1,412	459	784	644	537	716	201	1,595	652	357	1,007	1,251		895	1,654	1,683	1,638	387	1,116
Pittsburgh, Pa.	687	561	452	129	1,208	1,411	287	838	2,426	752	857	1,070	368	895		2,535	2,578	2,465	984	221
Portland, Ore.	2,601	3,046	2,083	2,418	2,009	1,238	2,349	1,809	959	2,259	1,678	2,505	2,885	1,654	2,535		636	172	1,913	2,754
San Francisco, Calif.	2,496	3,095	2,142	2,467	1,753	1,235	2,399	1,861	379	2,125	1,940	2,249	2,934	1,683	2,578	636		808	1,760	2,799
Seattle, Wash.	2,618	2,976	2,013	2,348	2,078	1,307	2,279	1,858	1,131	2,290	1,608	2,574	2,815	1,638	2,465	172	808		1,982	2,684
Tulsa, Okla.	772	1,537	683	925	257	681	909	248	1,452	401	695	647	1,344	387	984	1,913	1,760	1,982		1,189
Washington, D.C.	608	429	671	346	1,319	1,616	506	1,042	2,631	867	1,090	1,078	233	1,116	221	2,754	2,799	2,684	1,189	

46   coin

COINS OF THE OLD WORLD

GREEK DECADRACHM
(5th century B.C.)

SPANISH PIECES OF EIGHT

ITALIAN TESTONE
(16th century)

ROMAN DENARIUS
(1st century A.D.)

**JUDEAN
WIDOW'S MITE**
(1st century A.D.)

ISLAMIC FATIMID
(11th century)

ENGLISH PENNY
(14th century)

BYZANTINE NOMISMA

VENETIAN DUCAT
(13th century)

coin (koin), a stamped or embossed disk that is generally made of metal and used as money. Coins are necessary for completing small, everyday financial transactions, and the minting of them is an important function of national governments. Unlike paper currency, which merely represents value, coins have a value in themselves.

Most modern coins bear designs and words that are impressed into the surface of the coin during minting. In the typical minting operation the metal to be used is melted and cast into bars. The bars are divided into coin strips of regulated thickness. The strips are fed to a cutting machine, where carbon-steel dies punch out blank coins. The coins are then milled by a machine that raises their edges above the surface. This process makes it easier to stack the coins and also minimizes surface wear. Finally, the coins are fed to a hydraulic press that imprints symbols and words under tremendous pressure. At the same time the rims of the more valuable coins receive a pattern of indentations to prevent people from shaving off bits of the metal.

History

In early civilizations, goods were acquired by barter, or the direct exchange of one commodity for another. When coins became the principal medium of exchange, such metals as gold, silver, bronze, copper, lead, and iron were used to mint them. The first known coins were introduced in Lydia in Asia Minor and in China about the 8th century B.C. The Lydian coins, probably issued by private rather than by state sources, were made of a natural alloy of gold and silver, known as electrum. Governments soon assumed the responsibility for authorizing and producing coins. By the end of the 6th century B.C., gold and silver coins were being minted in many Greek city-states. As Athens became

the commercial center of the Aegean Sea area, its coins were used and imitated throughout the region.

The first Roman coins were made of bronze, and they date from about the 4th century B.C. Gold and silver were used during the period of the later Roman Empire. After the fall of Rome in the 5th century A.D., Byzantine and Merovingian gold coins and, later, Carolingian silver coins were used extensively in European trade centers. With the breaking up of the Carolingian Empire various cities and states made their own coins, which were mostly crude thin silver pieces. As Genoa and Venice rose in commercial importance in the 12th century, Italian coins became the predominant medium of exchange.

The early American colonists used Indian wampum as money. Wampum consisted of small shell beads made into belts. The value of wampum was not based on the worth of its material as much as on the labor required to produce the belts. In the colonial period European coins were circulated in America, but their value fluctuated from colony to colony and from one locality to another. In 1652 the Massachusetts Bay colony produced the first coins minted in America. During the American Revolution the Continental Congress issued coins made of pewter, silver, and brass.

The U.S. Mint was established in Philadelphia in 1792, and its first coins were circulated the following year. In the American Civil War the Confederacy printed paper money because of the shortage of metal to make coins. After the war, bank notes, checks, drafts, and other forms of paper currency increased in use, while metal currency continued to decline. In 1933 the United States discontinued entirely the use of gold coins in domestic and foreign commerce. It is still legal, however, for coin collectors to save them and to exchange them with other collectors.

AMERICAN COINS OF THE PAST
(Both sides of each coin are shown.)

PINE TREE SHILLING

FUGIO CENT

CONFEDERATE
HALF-DOLLAR

COMMEMORATIVE
ISABELLA QUARTER

$20 GOLD PIECE

Coins have always reflected the degree of prosperity enjoyed by the nations issuing them. The Romans often devaluated their coins to pay their debts with "cheap" money during financial crises. Similar depreciation of coins was common at various times in all later European states. It occurred whenever rulers resorted to reminting coins at a reduced ratio of gold and silver to make up for the lack of available funds. In more modern times the silver content of British coins was decreased with the decline of the British Empire after World War I. By 1947 British "silver" coins had lost all their silver content and were being made of a mixture of copper and nickel, called cupronickel.

Coin Design

The earliest coins were seldom imprinted with words, but most of them bore symbols on both their observe, or front and reverse, back sides. Generally, the designs represented animals, religious subjects, military heroes, or civil authorities. The head of the goddess Athena was frequently depicted on Athenian coins. Roman coins commemorated great victories or bore a representation of the head of an emperor or of a god. Many ancient coins are outstanding for their artistic qualities. Syracuse, a trade center in Sicily, produced some of the most beautiful coins, and certain of its skilled craftsmen and artists have become known to generations through the coins they designed.

Through the ages the coins of all countries typically have carried the profile of a present or past chief of state and a motto. Many U.S. coins bear a representation of the head of a former President. The date of issue and the denomination appear on all U.S. coins, and almost all coins bear such inscriptions as "Liberty," "In God We Trust," and "E Pluribus Unum," a Latin phrase meaning "one from many."

Coin Collecting

There are an estimated 400,000 numismatists, or coin collectors, in the United States. The prime consideration in determining the worth of a coin is supply and demand. The condition of a coin also affects its value. A coin that shows little or no surface wear is far more valuable than another of the same year that shows signs of considerable handling or wear. Ancient coins are often valuable regardless of condition.

In large collections, coins are usually wrapped individually and kept in trays stored in metal cabinets. Smaller collections and display pieces are kept in specially designed albums and folders. Many albums include cutout spaces for inserting a series of related coins. An important part of collecting is the ability to recognize counterfeit coins. Counterfeits usually make a dull sound when they are dropped on a hard surface, and many of them feel greasy. They also have irregular edges, and some of them can be easily cut with a knife. Many numismatists collect only the coins of a specific country, and some collect coins regardless of origin. Other collectors specialize in tokens, commemorative medals, and paper money in addition to the coins of one or more countries.

Books for Further Study
How to Build a Coin Collection by Fred Reinfeld and Burton H. Hobson (Sterling, 1977).
Coin Collecting, edited by the Boy Scouts of America (Boy Scouts of America, 1975).

FOR ADVANCED STUDENTS
Fell's International Coin Book, edited by Charles J. Andrews (6th ed., Fell, 1976).
The Complete Book of Coin Collecting by Joseph Coffin (5th rev. ed., Coward, 1976).

*Hillel Kaslove

GRAPHS

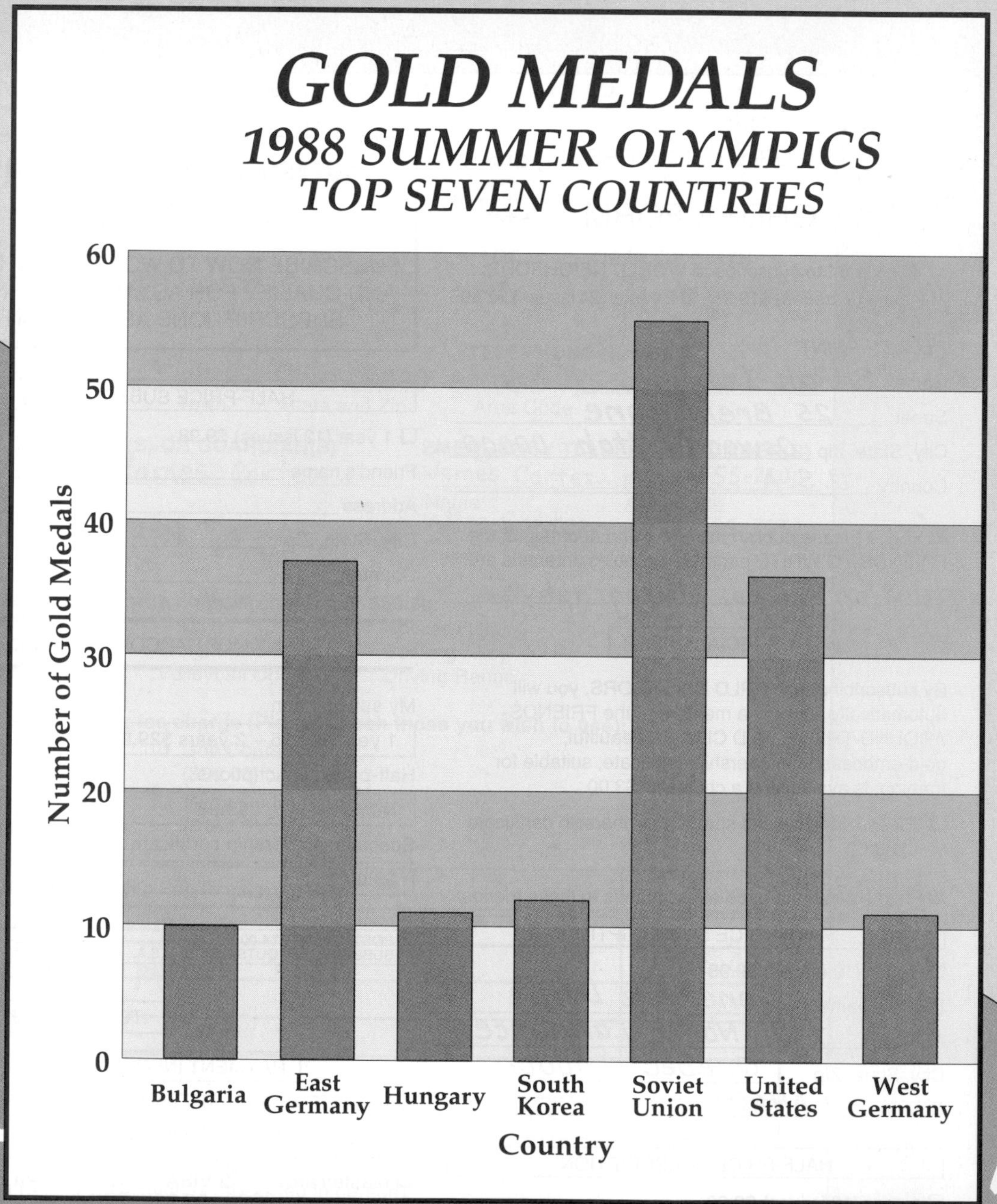
GOLD MEDALS
1988 SUMMER OLYMPICS
TOP SEVEN COUNTRIES
Number of Gold Medals
0
10
20
30
40
50
60
Bulgaria
East Germany
Hungary
South Korea
Soviet Union
United States
West Germany
Country

BAR GRAPH

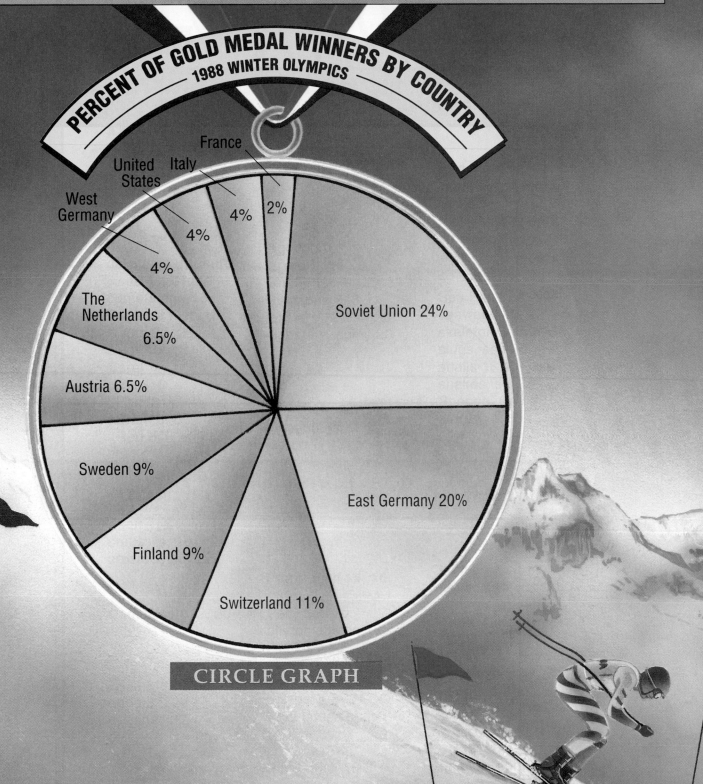

PERCENT OF GOLD MEDAL WINNERS BY COUNTRY
1988 WINTER OLYMPICS

France

United States Italy

West Germany

4% 4% 2%

4%

The Netherlands

6.5%

Soviet Union 24%

Austria 6.5%

Sweden 9%

East Germany 20%

Finland 9%

Switzerland 11%

CIRCLE GRAPH

565

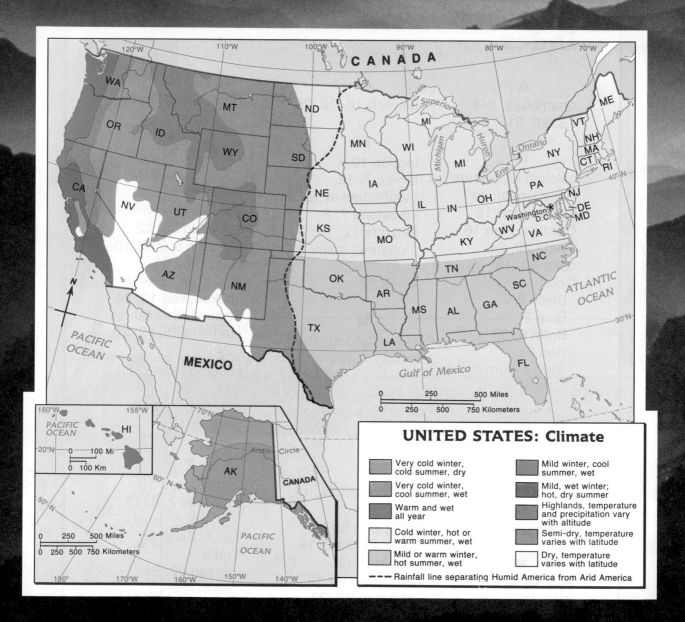

UNITED STATES: Climate

- Very cold winter, cold summer, dry
- Very cold winter, cool summer, wet
- Warm and wet all year
- Cold winter, hot or warm summer, wet
- Mild or warm winter, hot summer, wet
- Mild winter, cool summer, wet
- Mild, wet winter; hot, dry summer
- Highlands, temperature and precipitation vary with altitude
- Semi-dry, temperature varies with latitude
- Dry, temperature varies with latitude
- - - - Rainfall line separating Humid America from Arid America

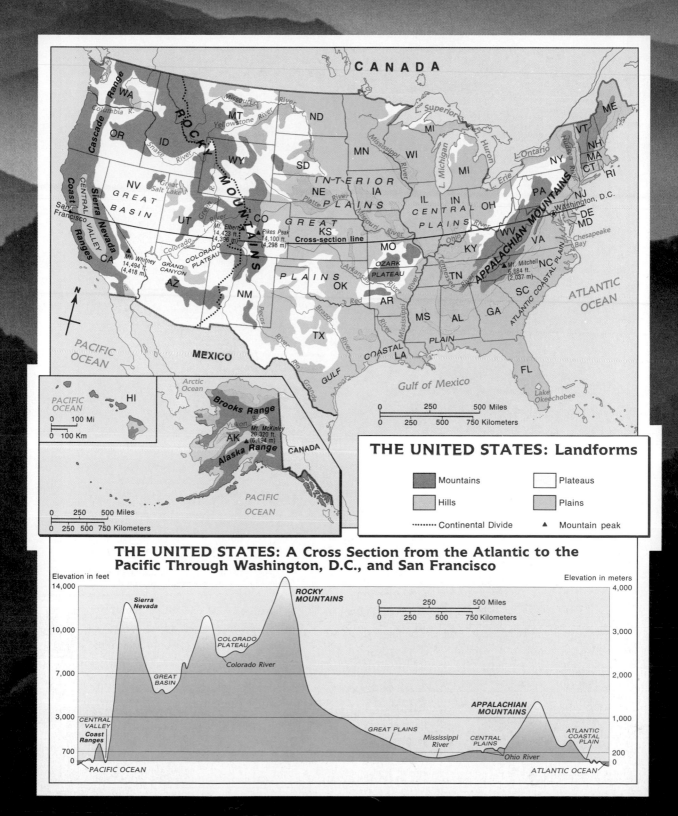

CANADA

WA
OR
ID
MT
ND
MN
WI
MI
ME
VT
NH
MA
CT
RI
NY

Cascade Range
Columbia R.
ROCKY MOUNTAINS
Missouri River
Yellowstone River
Snake River

NV
GREAT BASIN
UT
WY
SD
NE
IA
IL
IN
OH
PA
NJ
DE
MD

Sierra Nevada
Coast Ranges
Central Valley
San Francisco

Great Salt Lake
Green R.
CO
Mt. Elbert 14,433 ft. (4,396 m)
Pikes Peak 14,100 ft. (4,298 m)
Cross-section line

INTERIOR PLAINS
GREAT
Platte River
Missouri River

CENTRAL PLAINS
Ohio River
KY
WV
VA
APPALACHIAN MOUNTAINS
Washington, D.C.
Chesapeake Bay

Mt. Whitney 14,494 ft. (4,418 m)
CA
AZ
GRAND CANYON
COLORADO PLATEAU
Colorado River

NM
KS
MO
OZARK PLATEAU
TN
NC
Mt. Mitchell 6,684 ft. (2,037 m)
SC
ATLANTIC COASTAL PLAIN
ATLANTIC OCEAN

N

PLAINS
OK
AR
Arkansas River
Red River

TX
Brazos River
Pecos River
Rio Grande

MS
AL
GA

COASTAL
LA
GULF
PLAIN

FL
Lake Okeechobee

PACIFIC OCEAN
MEXICO

Gulf of Mexico

0   250   500 Miles
0   250   500   750 Kilometers

PACIFIC OCEAN
HI
0   100 Mi
0   100 Km

Arctic Ocean
Brooks Range
Yukon
AK
Mt. McKinley 20,320 ft. (6,194 m)
Alaska Range
CANADA
PACIFIC OCEAN

0   250   500 Miles
0   250   500   750 Kilometers

THE UNITED STATES: Landforms

▨ Mountains	▢ Plateaus
▨ Hills	▨ Plains
········· Continental Divide	▲ Mountain peak

THE UNITED STATES: A Cross Section from the Atlantic to the Pacific Through Washington, D.C., and San Francisco

Elevation in feet
14,000
10,000
7,000
3,000
700
0

Elevation in meters
4,000
3,000
2,000
1,000
200
0

Sierra Nevada
ROCKY MOUNTAINS
COLORADO PLATEAU
Colorado River
GREAT BASIN
CENTRAL VALLEY
Coast Ranges
PACIFIC OCEAN

0   250   500 Miles
0   250   500   750 Kilometers

GREAT PLAINS
Mississippi River
CENTRAL PLAINS
APPALACHIAN MOUNTAINS
Ohio River
ATLANTIC COASTAL PLAIN
ATLANTIC OCEAN

569

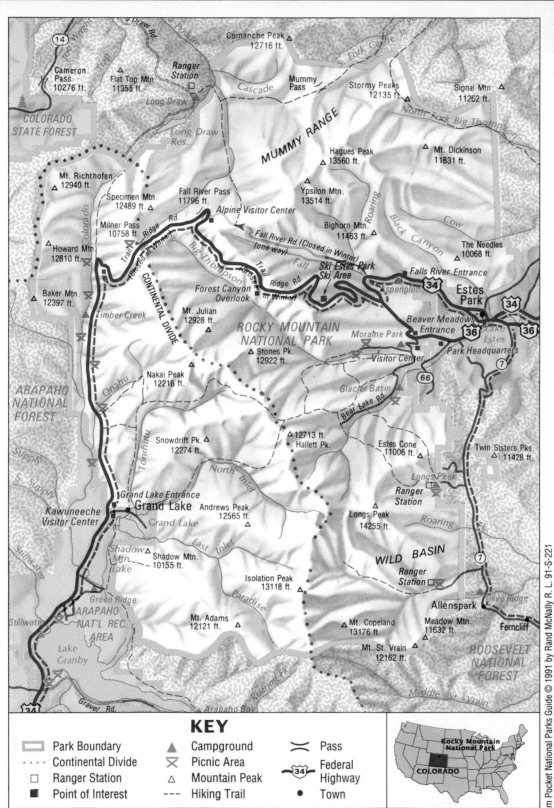

KEY

- ▭ Park Boundary
- ⋯ Continental Divide
- ▫ Ranger Station
- ■ Point of Interest
- ▲ Campground
- ⊠ Picnic Area
- △ Mountain Peak
- --- Hiking Trail
- ≍ Pass
- 〔34〕 Federal Highway
- ● Town

From Pocket National Parks Guide © 1991 by Rand McNally R. L. 91-S-221

THE LONG'S PEAK TRAIL

Crestview Chronicle

Volume 127, No. 347   25 cents   Crestview, Maine (00000)   Monday, September 13, 1993

Community welcomes exchange students

By Bill Killian
Chronicle reporter

At a public reception yesterday, Mayor Ted Wainwright officially welcomed foreign exchange students Amelia Fuentez and Thomas Heinemann to Crestview. The event, held at the Crestview Community Building, was attended by a crowd of more than two hundred local residents.

The two students, who have come to Crestview as part of the American Field Service foreign exchange program, will spend the academic year here, where both are enrolled as special students at Crestview High School. During their stay, they will be living with local families. Currently, Fu___ ___ be host family to Fuentez, and the Preston Danvars will welcome Heinemann to their home.

Crestview has taken part in the American Field Service exchange program since 1985, and Fuentez and Heinemann are the 19th and 20th foreign students to be assigned here. Commented Mayor Wainwright, "Having these students in our community has been a wonderful experience for everyone. It's a bit like having our own small U.N.".

The host families are equally enthusiastic about their new family members. "Thomas has been with us for only a week," said Judy Danebar, "but it seems much longer. He really fits in. My five-year-old has

AFS students Amelia Fuentez (left) **and Thomas Heinemann** (right) visit while attending a reception held in their honor yesterday at the Crestview Community Building.

The Garcias are particularly happy to have Amelia with them. "Although Spanish is our native language," said Roberto Garcia, "___

small Swiss mountain village of Goldau, this is a first visit to the United States. "It's like a dream come true," he remarked. "Since I

Home ownership eludes many

WASHINGTON (AP) — Many Americans — particularly minorities, the young and single people — find the dream of home ownership slipping from their grasp, a Census Bureau study concludes.

The report, "Who Can Afford to Buy a House?," found that 57 percent of all households — both owners and renters — could not afford a median-priced house purchased with a conventional, 30-year, fixed-rate mortgage.

Thirty-six percent of current homeowners and 91 percent of renters did not qualify for a median-priced home.

Even a modestly priced house is too expensive for 48 percent of the nation's households, said the report, released Thursday. And 15 percent could not afford to buy a home at even the lowest prices.

A median-priced house is one that is more expensive than half the homes in a market and less expensive than half. A modestly priced house was defined as one where 75 percent of the homes in the market cost more.

"This seems to be telling us that the step from renting to home ownership is a big step for a large number of households and perhaps a bigger step than was

generally realized," said economist Mark Obrinsky of the Federal National Mortgage Association.

The study, which analyzed the income debt levels and savings of 12,000 households surveyed in the spring of 1988, found sharp differences in the ability to buy a home by region, age, marital status and race or ethnic background.

For instance, 77 percent of black families and 74 percent of Hispanic families could not buy a median-priced home, compared with 43 percent of whites and 46 percent of non-Hispanics.

OFFICE HOLDS IMMUNIZATIONS

CRESTVIEW—The Crane County Health Department will hold an immunization clinic Monday, September 20, from 1 to 4 p.m. at its offices, 200 Main Street.

Parents are asked to bring their child's immunization records to the clinic. A $5 fee will be charged for the immunizations; however no one will be denied service due to inability to pay.

Immunizations are also given at the Health Department by appointment if the clinic times are not convenient. Immunization clinics are held the first and third Mondays of each month.

NEWSPAPER – FRONT PAGE

OPINION

Recently, the Crestview Chronicle ran an article on year-round schools. We asked our readers to comment.

Let's Change!

In many countries in the world, students attend school for many more days than they do here. In Japan, there's a 243-day school year, in the Soviet Union 120, and in the Netherlands 200. Our tradition of summer vacations goes back to the time when children were needed to work on the farm during the busy harvest season. As a result, we have one of the shortest school years among the industrialized nations. We're really out of step.

I think it's time for a change. Child labor no longer exists, and we need to be concerned with a problem of vital importance to our country: the education of our young people. If this means a longer school year, I'm all for it.
Barbara Neuhart

Poor Idea

As a parent (but still a kid at heart), I oppose children going to school year-round. I think it's important for them to be involved in other things and finding out about life in general. I

Letters to the Editor

Crestview Chronicle
CLASSIFIEDS

GARAGE/ YARD SALES

Yard Sale – 583 Irving – Sat., Sept. 18, 10:00 – 4:00. Everything but the kitchen sink.

———

Garage Sale – City Building – Sat., Sept. 18, 9:00–5:00 and Sun., Sept. 19, 2:00–5:00. Clothes, bedding, curtains, books, toys, misc.

Proceeds to benefit Crestview Youth Club.

———

Garage Sale – 2-family – 108 Aspen Road – Fri., Sept. 17, 12:00–8:00. Household goods, appliances large and small.

———

Leaving-town Sale – Sun., Sept. 19, Everything goes. 1504 Locust – all day until it's gone!

Yard Sale – Sat. Sept. 18 – 9:00–5:00. 144 W. 10th.

FOR SALE

German Shepherd puppies – 9 wks. old, $50. Call 555-8586 after 5:00 p.m.

———

Camping Equipment, including Army Style Squad tent. Call 555-1351 between 8:00 and 10:00 p.m.

———

Spinet piano in very good condition, $750. Call days only, 555-6766

———

Variable-speed treadmill. Never used. Call 555-4594 anytime.

———

Child's skis, poles, and boots, never used. Call 555-9498 after 6:00 p.m.

———

Macintosh IIx with 8 meg-

Nikon F Camera w/case, excellent condition. Best offer. Call 555-7878, 6:00 –10:00 p.m.

WANTED TO BUY

Used Books – All kinds. Brearly Book Store, 18 Main – 555-4476

———

Used 10-speed bicycle at good price. Call 555-8722

———

Dining room table with 6 or 8 chairs for small room. 555-2694

———

Musical Instruments – band instruments, pianos, orchestra instruments. Wells Music Supply – 2800 Lawton 555-7800

———

Pedigreed Abyssinian and Burmese kittens, female. After 6:00 p.m. 555-3857

Classified Ads

Eclipse will be partial in Kansas

KANSAS CITY, Mo. (AP)—The eclipse of the decade expected Thursday will plunge millions of people into darkness for a few minutes, but the effects in Kansas won't be so dramatic, astronomers say.

The state will experience about 28 percent blockage of the sun when the moon passes in front of it, beginning about noon MST., say astronomers at the Powell Observatory in Louisburg, Kan., about 40 miles south of the Kansas City area.

Solar eclipses occur during the day when the moon passes between the sun and the Earth. The moon's shadow, which is cone-shaped, draws a narrow path of darkness across the Earth as it rotates.

In Kansas City, the moon will begin to cover the sun at 12:07 p.m. Thursday. The biggest blockage will occur at 1:08 p.m., and the eclipse will end at 2:08 p.m.

Astronomers caution people not to look directly at the sun since its ultraviolet rays can cause permanent damage to the eyes.

People in Hawaii, Baja Mexico or parts of Central America will experience a full eclipse, as the sky slowly dims, the stars pop out and temperatures drop.

Kansas City is more than 1,000 miles from the center of totality. In Hawaii, there will be about four minutes of darkness and about six minutes in Mexico. There won't be a longer eclipse until the year 2132.

Feature Story

NEWSPAPER

REAL-LIFE

ADVENTURE

VOL. 79 NO.6   NOVEMBER / DECEMBER 1993

The Race to the South Pole

Magazine — Cover Page

REAL – LIFE
ADVENTURE

| Volume 79 | November–December 1993 | Number 6 |

IN THIS ISSUE:

Publisher
Elden Ruder
•
Editor–in–Chief
Mary Wolak
•
Editorial Director
Lawrence Hinger
•
Editor
Juanita Ruiz
•
Associate Editor
Bryan Rowlinson
•
Assistant Editor
Camille Krannswitter
•
Art Associate
Ray Dechant
•
Compositor
Marianne Martinez
•
Circulation Director
Hernandez Lefébvre
•
Advertising
Maurice Riedel

Cover: The challenge of reaching the South Pole led rival explorers across the frozen wastes of Antarctica (main photo). Roald Amundsen, leader of the first successful expedition, is shown taking sights at the pole (inset).

Real-Life ADVENTURE (ISSN: 0000-0000) is published bimonthly by Adventure Enterprises, Inc., 5454 Interway Boulevard, Tallahassee, Florida 00000. Copyright ©1993 by Adventure Enterprises, Inc. All rights reserved. Title registered U.S. Patent Office. **Editorial Offices: P.O. Box 23, Kansas City, Missouri 00000.**

SUBSCRIPTION PRICE: One year (6 issues) $15.00; two years (12 issues) $25.00. For subscriptions outside the U.S., add $3.00

Magazine — Contents Page

SCHEDULES

NORTH ELEMENTARY SCHOOL
AFTER-SCHOOL ACTIVITIES SCHEDULE

OCTOBER

SUNDAY	MONDAY	TUESDAY	WEDNESDAY	THURSDAY	FRIDAY	SATURDAY
					1 3:00 Football Practice	**2**
3	**4** 3:00–5:00 Supervised Playground 3:00 Football Practice 6:30 Annual Parent-Teacher-Student Banquet (Cafeteria)	**5** 3:00 Football Practice 3:30 Play Rehearsal	**6** 3:00 Football Practice 3:30 Girl's Athletic Club (Room 105)	**7** 3:30 Play Rehearsal	**8** **In-Service Day** No School	**9**
10	**11** **Columbus Day** No School	**12** 3:00 Football Practice 3:15 Brownies (Room 110)	**13** 3:00 Football Practice 3:30 Play Rehearsal	**14** 3:00 Pep Rally (Gym) 3:30 Football Game – North Tigers vs Grant Cougars (Grant School)	**15** 3:30 Play Rehearsal 3:45 All-School Bicycle Race (City Park)	**16** 10:00 Science Club Field Trip to Burnam Woods (meet at North School for bus)
17	**18** 3:00–5:00 Supervised Playground 3:00 Football practice	**19** 3:00 Play Rehearsal (Dress Rehearsal)	**20** 3:00 Football Practice 3:15 Art Club (Room 110)	**21** 7:00 Performance: "The Ugly Duckling" (Auditorium)	**22** 3:00 Football Practice	**23**
24	**25** 3:00–5:00 Supervised Playground 3:00 Football practice 3:30 Science Club (Room 110)	**26** 3:00 Football Practice 3:15 Cub Scouts (Room 110)	**27** 3:00 Football Practice 3:30 Film Festival: "Around the World in 80 Days" (Auditorium)	**28** 3:00 Pep Rally (Gym) 3:30 Football Game – North Tigers vs Central Indians (North School)	**29** 3:30 Halloween Party (Gym)	**30**
31 **Halloween**						

576

FRIENDSHIP TOURS

Announces

The Addition of Two New, Exciting Trips to its Summer Schedule

— to —

BRITISH COLUMBIA, ALBERTA, AND SOUTHERN ALASKA

TOUR 14

17 days: *Departures June 16, 25, 30; July 9, 14, 23, 28; August 6. A swing through the Rockies, highlighted by nights at Jasper and Banff, a rail adventure, and an Inside Passage cruise.*

SCHEDULE

DAY 1. Seattle to Victoria.
Your Tour Director welcomes you aboard a roomy motorcoach, and you go by road and ferry to Victoria, B.C., where you enjoy a Get-Acquainted Dinner. Overnight. (D)

DAY 2. Butchart Gardens, Vancouver.
Stroll through these famed gardens, then ferry across the Strait of Georgia. Overnight in Vancouver. (B, D)

DAY 3. Rail adventure, Kamloops.
Ride in style by comfortable rail car to Kamloops, in the heart of B.C. ranching country. (B, L, D)

DAY 4. Rail adventure, Jasper.
Still aboard your rail car, you ride high into the mountains—passing 12,972-foot Mt. Robson and other towering peaks. Overnight in Jasper. (B, L, D)

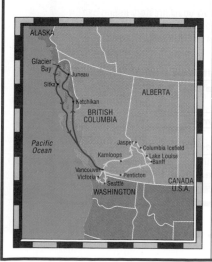

DAY 5. Jasper sightseeing.
See the sights in this mountain-ringed village and view peaks that pierce the sky: Pyramid Mountain, the Maligne Range, Mt. Edith Cavell. Then you may decide to ride the tramway up Whistler Mountain, play golf, or raft a river. Overnight in Jasper. (B, D)

DAY 6. Snowcoach ride, Lake Louise.
You'll visit the spectacular Icefield Parkway and ride a snowcoach on Athabasca Glacier. Overnight at lovely Chateau Lake Louise. (B, D)

DAY 7. Banff.
To Banff, with the distinctive silhouette of guardian Mt. Rundle. Explore your famous hotel, with its shops, restaurants, lounges, pools, and mile-high golf course. Overnight at Banff Springs Hotel. (B, D)

DAY 8. Banff sightseeing.
Your Tour Director accompanies you to Banff high spots, including Bow Falls, the hot springs, and the townsite with its many shops. Then you may raft the river, go horseback riding, birdwatch, or just take it easy. Overnight at Banff Springs Hotel. (B, D)

DAY 9. Penticton.
Leave the Rockies and drive down to overnight at Penticton, on Okanagan Lake. A special dinner to say goodbyes to some. (B, D)

DAY 10. Vancouver, sail.
Back to Vancouver, where you board ship for a cruise to Alaska. The cruise part of your tour is unescorted. Breakfast and dinner, and all meals aboard ship, are included.

DAY 11. Inside Passage cruising.

DAY 12. Ketchikan.

DAY 13. Juneau.

DAY 14. Cruising Glacier Bay.

DAY 15. Sitka.

DAY 16. Inside Passage cruising.

DAY 17. Vancouver to Seattle. Tour ends.

TOUR 15

10 days: *Departures June 16, 25, 30; July 9, 14, 23, 28; August 6. Tour 15 is identical to Tour 14 without inclusion of the Alaska Cruise.*

Majestic Wenchenma Peaks tower above Moraine Lake in Banff National Park.

SCHEDULE

DAY 1 – DAY 9.
Schedule is identical with schedule for Tour 14, days 1-9.

DAY 10. Vancouver to Seattle. Tour ends.

For bookings, fares, more information, write or call:

FRIENDSHIP TOURS
P.O. Box 1000
Seattle, Washington 00000

1-800-555-1000

Meals included: **B**=breakfast, **L**=lunch, **D**=dinner

Thiss glossary can help you to pronounce and find out the meanings of words in this book that you may not know.

The words are listed in alphabetical order. Guide words at the top of each page tell you the first and last words on the page.

Each word is divided into syllables. The way to pronounce each word is given next. You will be able to understand the pronunciation respelling by using the key to the right. A shorter key appears at the bottom right corner of every other page.

When a word has more than one syllable, a dark accent mark (´) shows which syllable is stressed. In some words, a light accent mark (´) shows which syllable has a less heavy stress.

Glossary entries are based on entries in *The Macmillan/McGraw-Hill School Dictionary 1.*

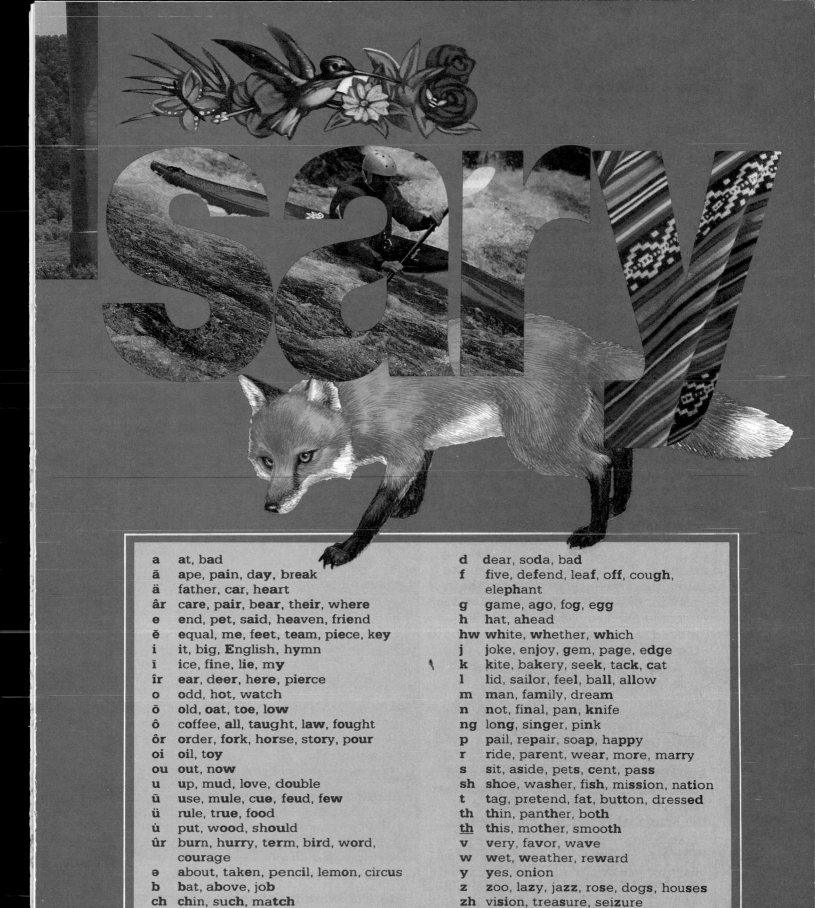

a	at, bad		d	dear, soda, bad
ā	ape, pain, day, break		f	five, defend, leaf, off, cough, elephant
ä	father, car, heart		g	game, ago, fog, egg
âr	care, pair, bear, their, where		h	hat, ahead
e	end, pet, said, heaven, friend		hw	white, whether, which
ē	equal, me, feet, team, piece, key		j	joke, enjoy, gem, page, edge
i	it, big, English, hymn		k	kite, bakery, seek, tack, cat
ī	ice, fine, lie, my		l	lid, sailor, feel, ball, allow
îr	ear, deer, here, pierce		m	man, family, dream
o	odd, hot, watch		n	not, final, pan, knife
ō	old, oat, toe, low		ng	long, singer, pink
ô	coffee, all, taught, law, fought		p	pail, repair, soap, happy
ôr	order, fork, horse, story, pour		r	ride, parent, wear, more, marry
oi	oil, toy		s	sit, aside, pets, cent, pass
ou	out, now		sh	shoe, washer, fish, mission, nation
u	up, mud, love, double		t	tag, pretend, fat, button, dressed
ū	use, mule, cue, feud, few		th	thin, panther, both
ü	rule, true, food		<u>th</u>	this, mother, smooth
ů	put, wood, should		v	very, favor, wave
ûr	burn, hurry, term, bird, word, courage		w	wet, weather, reward
ə	about, taken, pencil, lemon, circus		y	yes, onion
b	bat, above, job		z	zoo, lazy, jazz, rose, dogs, houses
ch	chin, such, match		zh	vision, treasure, seizure

"The Wreck of the *Zephyr*" from THE WRECK OF THE *ZEPHYR* by Chris Van Allsburg. Copyright © 1983 by Chris Van Allsburg. Reprinted by permission of Houghton Mifflin Company. All rights reserved.

INFORMATION ILLUSTRATED

Almanac: Excerpts from THE WORLD ALMANAC & BOOK OF FACTS, 1991 Edition, copyright Pharos Books 1990, New York, NY 10166. Reprinted by permission of The World Almanac and Book of Facts.

Cartoons: From JUST WAIT TILL YOU HAVE CHILDREN OF YOUR OWN! by Erma Bombeck and Bil Keane, Fawcett Crest, 1971. Reprinted by permission of Bil Keane and Aaron M. Priest Literary Agency, Inc., agent for Erma Bombeck. From THE NEW YORKER ALBUM OF DRAWINGS, 1925-1975, Viking Penguin, 1975. Copyright © 1973 (Reilly) by the New Yorker Magazine, Inc. Reprinted by permission of The New Yorker Magazine, Inc. From THE NEW YORKER BOOK OF CAT CARTOONS, copyright © 1990 by Alfred A. Knopf, 1990. Reprinted by permission of Alfred A. Knopf, Inc. From WHAT WAS BUGGING OL' PHAROAH? by Charles M. Schulz, copyright © 1964 by Warner Press. Reprinted by permission of Warner Press. From "Hi and Lois" by Mort Walker and Dik Browne, August 18, 1991. Reprinted with special permission of King Features Syndicate.

Dictionary: Excerpt from MACMILLAN SCHOOL DICTIONARY 1, copyright © 1991 by Macmillan/McGraw-Hill School Publishing Company. Reprinted by permission of Macmillan/McGraw-Hill School Publishing Company. Excerpt from THE NEW OXFORD PICTURE DICTIONARY, English/Spanish edition, edited by E. C. Parnwell. Copyright © 1989 by Oxford University Press. Reprinted by permission of Oxford University Press, Inc.

Encyclopedia: Excerpt from "coin" by Hillel Kaslove, from MERIT STUDENT ENCYCLOPEDIA, vol. 5. Copyright © 1991 by Macmillan Educational Company. Reprinted by permission of the publisher.

Index: From LIFE ON A CORAL REEF by Lionel Bender, copyright © 1989 by Gloucester Press. Reprinted by permission of Gloucester Press.

Maps: "United States: Climate" and "The United States: Landforms" from UNITED STATES AND ITS NEIGHBORS, copyright © 1991 by Macmillan/McGraw-Hill School Publishing Company. Reprinted by permission of Macmillan/McGraw-Hill School Publishing Company. From POCKET NATIONAL PARKS GUIDE, copyright © 1991 by Rand McNally R. L. 91-S-221. Reprinted by permission of Rand McNally & Company. "The Long's Peak Trail" by Enos A. Mills, from ROCKY MOUNTAIN NATIONAL PARK, Doubleday, Page & Company, 1924. Reprinted by permission of Edna Mills Kiley.

Newspapers and Magazines: "Home ownership eludes many" from *Goodland Daily News*, June 14, 1991. "Eclipse will be partial in Kansas" from *Goodland Daily News*, July, 1991. The preceding selections are reprinted by permission of Associated Press.

COVER DESIGN: WYD Design
COVER ILLUSTRATION: Marco Ventura

DESIGN CREDITS

Sheldon Cotler + Associates Editorial Group, *Units 2 & 4*
WYD Design, 16-19, 44-45, 206-209, 222-223, 364-367, 386-387
Designframe Incorporated, 74-75, 156-157, 242-243, 334-335, 408-409, 502-503
Notovitz Design Inc., *Information Illustrated*
Curriculum Concepts, Inc., *Glossary*

ILLUSTRATION CREDITS

Unit 1: David Schleinkofer, 44-45; Ron Morecraft, 46-47; Steven Bennett, 46 (typography) **Unit 2:** Glenn Dean, 116-119; Bryan Haynes, 138, 140, 148-153; John Martin, 154-155; James Marsh, 156-157. **Unit 3:** Andrea Baruffi, 206-209; Phil Howe, 222-223; Bob Shein, 224-225 (collage); Dale Verzaal, 260-279 (bkgd); Benjamin Harjo Jr., 280-281. **Unit 4:** David Diaz, 316-317; John Stevens, 332-333 (typography); Richard Chestnut, 336-347 (bkgd.); SC & A, 337-347 (hand-tinted art); Mark Braught, 362-363. **Unit 5:** Linda Gist, 364-367; Randy Smith, 386-387; Douglas Smith, 408-409. **Unit 6:** Marco Ventura, 456-459; Ron Morecraft, 478-479; Gary Torrisi, 480-499 (bkgds. & typography); George Baquero, 500-501 (computer collage); Mike Lester, 520-521. **Information Illustrated:** Jack Suzuki, 545; Graphic Chart and Map Co., 546-547; Alex Bloch, 550; Anatoly Chernishov, 554-555; Bob Pasternak, 558-559, 565; Tom Connor, 576. **Glossary:** Josef Sumichrast, 582; Alex Bloch, 584, 605; Gil Ashby, 584, 603; Gary Torrisi, 586; James Needham, 588, 598; Bob Pepper, 591; Neverne Covington, 593; Cary Henrie, 596; Bob Frank, 600; Rodica Prato, 606.

PHOTOGRAPHY CREDITS

All photographs are by the Macmillan/McGraw-Hill School Division (MMSD) except as noted below.

Table of Contents: 6: t.l. William Franklin McMahon/People Weekly/ © 1986 Time Inc.; t.r. U.S. Patent and Trademark Office. 9: t.r. Minnesota Historical Society; b.r. South Dakota State Historical Society. 12: t.l. University of Washington Microform & Newspaper Collections.   **Unit 1:** 16-19: William Waterfall/ The Stock Market. 42: Jack Spratt/Picture Group. 43: Scott Harvey for MMSD. 44-45: Dan Ford Connelly/Picture Group for MMSD. 73: b. Roy Morsch/The Stock Market. 74-75: Glen Wexler. 91: t. Marion E. Wade Center, Wheaton College. 91: b. Scott Harvey for MMSD. 92-93: Nicholas Rozsa. 113: t.,b.l. Paul Erikson; b.r. Ken Mallory. 114-115: Herb Segars. 116-119: Raymond Mendez for MMSD.   **Unit 2:** 135: t. Lillian Kemp; b. Bachrach. 136-137: Mark Stephensen/Westlight Backgrounds. 139: t., m., l. US Patent and Trademark Office. 141: l.,r. Myron Starbird. 142: l. Cleveland Public Library. 143: Richard Chesnut for MMSD. 144: Gerry Lynas. 145: l. Harcourt Brace Jovanovich; r. William Franklin McMahon/People Weekly/ © 1986 Time Inc. 146: t. *The Capital Times*/Henry A. Koshollek; b. *Aurora Advertiser*/Paul E. Donley. 147: Harcourt Brace Jovanovich. 151: Margaret Miller/Courtesy of William Morrow & Company. 153: r. Courtesy of Barbara Taylor; Allen Goldstein. 158: Steve Smith. 180: t. National Dance Institute, photo Martha Swope; b. Carolyn George D'Amboise. 181: Lynn Johnson/Black Star. 182-203: Richard Chesnut for MMSD. 203: Jim Belford.   **Unit 3:** 224: t.l. Culver Pictures, Inc.; t.r. The Bettmann Archive; t.m. inset B. Bartholomew/Black Star; b.l., b.r. Brown Brothers; b.m. Archiv/Photo Researchers. 224-225: John W. Banagan/The Image Bank. 225: t.r., t.m., b.m. Brown Brothers; b.l. The Granger Collection; b.r. Culver Pictures Inc. 237: Richard Chesnut for MMSD. 240: Joanne Ryder. 242-243: Jay Alan Lefcowitz. 244: t.m. Ariel Skelley. 260: l., C. Chesek/American Museum of Natural History; r. Minnesota Historical Society. 261: Smithsonian Institution. 263: l. The Bettmann Archive; r. Smithsonian Institution; b. Denver Art Museum. 265: South Dakota State Historical Society.   **Unit 4:** 282-283: Arie de Zanger for MMSD. 284 t.l.: C. Fishman/Woodfin Camp; m. Olson/Sygma; b.l. Mike Maple/Woodfin Camp; b.r. Jim Thompson/Sygma. 284-285: D. Fineman/ Sygma. 285: t.r. Jim Thompson/Sygma. 313: t. George Fry for Addison Wesley Publishing Co.; Richard Chesnut for MMSD. 314: t. Oberlin College, Allen Art Museum; b. Smithsonian Institution. 315: t.l., t.r. Reunion des Musees Nationaux; m. Magnum; b. Arie de Znger for MMSD. 331: t. Margaret Miller/ Courtesy of William Morrow & Co.; b. Richard Chesnut for MMSD. 332-333: Franklin Jay Viola/Comstock. 332: inset, Arie de Zanger for MMSD. 334-335: John Rizzo. 336: Richard Chesnut for MMSD. 347: t. Little, Brown & Co.; b. Richard Chesnut for MMSD. 361: Scott Harvey for MMSD.   **Unit 5:** 368-369: Joe Viesti/Viesti Associates, Inc. 369: MacBride Museum Collection/Yukon Archive. 370: t. Special Collections Division, University Washington Libraries, Photo: A. Curtis; m. Skookum Jim Oral History Project Collection/Yukon Archives; b. MacBride Museum Collection/Yukon Archives. 371: Special Collections Division University of Washington Libraries. 372: University of Washington Microfilm & Newspaper Collections. 373: The Ronald C. Kinsey Collection. 374: Puget Sound Maritime Historical Society, Inc. 376-377: Special Collections Division University of Washington Libraries, Photo: Goetzman. 378-380: Museum of History and Industry. 383: The Ronald C. Kinsey Collection. 384: Special Collections Division University of Washington Libraries. 385: The Ronald C. Kinsey Collection. 386: b.l. Wolfgang Kaehler; b.r. Jeff Schultz/Alaska Stock Images. 387: l.,r. Obremski/The Image Bank; b. Kathleen Thormood Carr. 388-389: The Cleveland Museum of Art, The Charles W. Harkness Gift, 27.389. 390: Carlo Ontal. 431: t. Alice Watson; b. Scott Harvey for MMSD. 432: l. inset, Indian and Northern Affairs, Canada; b. inset, Lee Boltin. 432-433: Steven J. Krasemann/DRK Photo. 433: b. inset, Indian & Northern Affairs, Canada. 453: l. Little Brown & Co. Fryers Studio, Fort William; r. Scott Harvey for MMSD. 454-455: © 1952 M.C. Escher/Cordon Art Baarn-Holland. 477: Bill Berger for MMSD.   **Unit 6:** 500-501: James Amos/ Photo Researchers; m. John Cancalosi/Tom Stack & Associates. 500: t.l., t.r., b.l., b.r. Library of Congress. 501: t.l., t.r., b.m., b.r. Library of Congress; b.l. Breck P. Kent/Earth Scenes. 502-503: Geoff Spear. 504: Scott Harvey for MMSD. 540: l. Lee Boltin; r. The San Antonio Museum Collection. 541: Francene Keery. 544: Uniphoto. 546: Allstock. 549: Scott Harvey for MMSD. 553: Jeff Hunter/The Image Bank. 562: Bob Daemmrich/Uniphoto. 566: t. The Image Bank; t.m. Bob Daemmrich/TSW; b.m. Diane Johnson/TSW; b. Topham/ The Image Works. 568-569: Barrie Rokeach/The Image Bank. 570-571: Sharon Gerig/Tom Stack & Associates. 572: Ken Karp for MMSD. 573: The Image Works. 574: Wolfgang Kaehler; inset, North Wind Picture Archives. 577: Eric Cale/Bruce Coleman, Inc. 578: Jeff Hunter/The Image Bank. 579: Scott Harvey for MMSD. 580. t. l. The Stock Market; t.r. Grant Heilman; b.r. Tom Stack & Associates. 581: l. Sportslight; r. The Image Bank 583: l. Tom Stack & Associates; r. Michal Heron for MMSD. 585: The Stock Market. 587: l. Michal Heron for MMSD; r. The Stock Market. 588: The Stock Market. 589: Photo Researchers. 590: PhotoEdit. 592: First Light. 593: Sportslight. 594: Tom Stack & Associates. 595: t.l. Michal Heron for MMSD; b.r. First Light. 596: Michal Heron for MMSD. 597: Grant Heilman. 598: The Image Bank. 599: The Stock Market. 601: t.l. Photo Researchers; b.r. Grant Heilman. 602: b.l. Michal Heron for MMSD; t.r. The Stock Market. 604: Tony Freeman/ PhotoEdit.

608